7 — 93

2

D1127317

MODERN MATHEMATICAL TOPICS

MODERN MATHEMATICAL TOPICS

by D. H. V. CASE, B.Sc.

Assistant Master,
Wellington College,
Berkshire

PHILOSOPHICAL LIBRARY INC.

© D. H. V. Case (1966)

Published 1968 by Philosophical Library Inc.,
15 East 40th Street, New York 16, N.Y.

To B.A.C.

Printed in Great Britain for Philosophical Library
by Richard Clay (The Chaucer Press), Ltd., Bungay, Suffolk

CONTENTS

Preface, vii

CONTENTS

PREFACE

Meredydd G. Hughes, M.A., wrote in *Modernising School Mathematics*, "There is firstly an urgent need for textbooks suitable for the new courses . . . it is desirable that the early books should evolve naturally from the teaching notes of those engaged in teaching experimental courses rather than that they should be produced *in vacuo* by textbook writers who have no opportunity of trying out their ideas in the classroom."

This book has grown out of my own teaching notes. For several years I had been very interested in modern developments in mathematics, and in September 1963 I began a course in mathematics for 1st year Arts and Biology "A" level students. The calculus and mechanics required was easy to organise, using two of the many textbooks available. However, when I tried to find a book on modern topics there was nothing available at all.

As a result of my reading I decided that it would help me and also make the subject more alive if I could show how these topics are being used in Industry. British Petroleum were extremely helpful, and I spent two weeks working in their operational research department, in April 1964. I am indebted to many people in British Petroleum, and especially to Mr. P. B. Coaker, who gave me permission to use the example in the second half of the chapter on linear programming, which illustrates the way in which real problems are solved.

Below are listed books which I have found helpful in writing this book, and also other books which I have since read and which must be included in any list of books on this subject.

Many teachers have not yet made up their minds to join one of the projects; perhaps this book may help them to introduce modern topics into their work.

It is difficult to mention all those who, either directly or indirectly, have advised, helped, criticised or just listened, but I must record my thanks to Peter Coaker of British Petroleum, Glynn Jarrett of Wellington College, who checked the manuscript and made many very valuable suggestions, and especially to Arthur Robinson of Atlantic College, who read the galley proofs. But any mistakes which remain, and the way in which the material is presented, for these the responsibility is my own.

My grateful thanks are also due to Barclays Bank Ltd. for permission to use the spreadeagle symbol on page 38, the *Financial Times* for permission to use the pie chart on page 117, and to the Oxford and Cambridge Schools Examination Board for permission to use questions set in their certificate examinations.

Wellington College
1966
D.H.V.C.

BOOKS

Adler, Irving, *The New Mathematics*, Signet Science Library

—— *Thinking Machines*, Signet Science Library

Brewer, *Introduction to the Theory of Sets*, Prentice Hall

Chambers, E. G., *Statistical Calculations for Beginners*, Cambridge University Press

Glicksman, A. M., *Linear Programming and the Theory of Games*, Wiley and Sons

Hughes, M. G., *Modernising School Mathematics*, G. Bell & Sons Ltd.

Johnson, D. A. and Glenn, W. H., *Sets, Sentences and Operations*, Webster Publishing Company

—— *The World of Statistics*, Webster Publishing Company

Kemeney, J. G., Snell and Thompson, *Introduction to Finite Mathematics*, Prentice Hall

Levy, and Preidel, *Elementary Statistics*, Nelson

Moroney, M. J., *Facts from Figures*, Pelican

Matthews, G., *Matrices*, Arnold

Organisation for European Economic Co-operation, *Mathematics for Physicists and Engineers*, synopses for modern secondary school mathematics in O.E.E.C. countries

Sawyer, W. W., *A Concrete Approach to Abstract Algebra*, W. H. Freeman & Co.

Schaff, W. L., *Basic Concepts of Elementary Mathematics*, Wiley and Sons

Stoll, R. R., *Sets, Logic and Axiomatic Theories*, W. H. Freeman

———————

Mansfield D. E. and Thompson, D., *Mathematics—A New Approach* (Books 1 and 2), Chatto and Windus

School Mathematics Project, Books T and T4, Cambridge University Press

Midlands Mathematics Experiment

Chapter 1

SETS

1. SET

The Smith family consists of: Grandfather and Granny Smith, their son John and his wife Joan Smith. John and Joan have three children, Robert, Jill and William.

They are all MEMBERS or ELEMENTS of the SET of the SMITH family.

Other examples of SETS are: the school football team, all the children taking Ordinary level mathematics this year, the letters of the alphabet.

* A SET, then, is a given group or collection of people, items or things. The objects within the set are called ELEMENTS (or MEMBERS).

We write: The ELEMENTS or MEMBERS of the SET of SMITHS

A {Grandfather, Granny, John, Joan, Robert, Jill, William.}

JILL "is an element of set" A is written "Jill ε A".
The symbol is the Greek letter "ε".

Example

What is the set of vowels?

$$\{a, e, i, o, u\}$$

For simplicity capital letters are used to denote sets.

2. EQUAL SETS

Bill, Fred and John went for a holiday together this year. They are a SET.

$$\{Bill, Fred, John\}$$

An EQUAL SET is one which contains the same ELEMENTS.

$$\{Fred, Bill, John\}$$

* See Paragraph 8.

9

Example

$$A = \{a\ b\ c\} \qquad\qquad A \text{ and } B \text{ are equal sets}$$
$$B = \{c\ a\ b\}$$

The order within the set does not matter; SETS are equal when they contain the same elements.

3. EQUIVALENT SETS

Sets which contain the same number of elements but NOT the same elements are called EQUIVALENT SETS.

The symbol that is used is,

$$A \longleftrightarrow B$$
$$A \text{ "is EQUIVALENT to" } B$$

Examples

1. $\{p, q\} \longleftrightarrow \{a, b\}$
2. $\{\text{Bill, Fred, John}\} \longleftrightarrow \{\text{Barbara, Joyce, Mabel}\}$
3. $\{a, e, i, o, u\} \longleftrightarrow \{1, 2, 3, 4, 5\}$

If the elements of two sets can be matched ONE TO ONE the sets are equivalent.

Example

$$\{ \quad A, \quad\quad B, \quad\quad C, \quad\quad D \quad \}$$
$$\updownarrow \quad\quad \updownarrow \quad\quad \updownarrow \quad\quad \updownarrow$$
$$\{\text{black, blue, white, red}\}$$

In the example

$$\{a, e, i, o, u\} \longleftrightarrow \{1, 2, 3, 4, 5\}$$

the vowels have been matched ONE TO ONE with the first 5 natural numbers. This concept is used whenever a set of objects is counted and is the basis of the counting numbers system (see Chapter 4).

4. FINITE SETS

When we can count all the Elements of the set it is a FINITE SET.

Example

What is the set of even numbers less than 10?

$$\{2, 4, 6, 8\}$$

5. INFINITE SETS

When we cannot count all the elements of the set it is an INFINITE SET.

Example

What is the set of natural numbers?

$$\{1, 2, 3, 4, 5, 6, \ldots\}$$

This set has no END.

6. A German mathematician, Cantor, compared two infinite sets:
The set of natural numbers

$$A = \{1, 2, 3, 4, 5, \ldots\}$$

The set obtained by multiplying each element of the set by 2

$$B = \{2, 4, 6, 8, 10, 12, \ldots\}$$

For every natural number, n, there exists a natural number, $2n$.
Therefore the sets A and B have a one to one matching, viz.

$$A = \{1, 2, 3, 4, \ 5, \ldots\}$$
$$\uparrow \ \uparrow \ \uparrow \ \uparrow \ \uparrow$$
$$\downarrow \ \downarrow \ \downarrow \ \downarrow \ \downarrow$$
$$B = \{2, 4, 6, 8, 10, \ldots\}$$
$$\therefore \qquad A \longleftrightarrow B$$

Therefore there are as many even numbers as there are natural
numbers.

7. In our system of counting the symbol 0 means zero or nought.
In set language the EMPTY or NULL set is written ϕ.

Example

What is the set of cats with five legs?

Answer: ϕ.

Sometimes the null set is represented by { }.

8. HISTORICAL

The definition of a set has been discussed by some of the greatest
mathematicians of this century. In 1912 Russell held that it was
unnecessary to do so in order to understand Cantor's theory. The
definition given in paragraph 1 above must then be thought of as an
aid to understanding and not as the "last word" on the subject.

Little has been said of Infinite Sets, but these form the nucleus of
Cantor's work. An example may help:

"Two unequal line segments contain the same number of points."
BC and ED are 2 unequal line segments. Let BE and CD, both
produced, meet in A.

As line *AF* moves from position *AB* to position *AC* it cuts *ED* and *BC* at *G* and *F*.

Hence, every point on *ED* has a corresponding point on *BC*, a ONE TO ONE correspondence. The set of points on *ED* is equivalent to the set of points on *BC*.

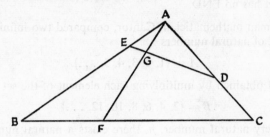

EXERCISE No. 1

1. List the elements of the following sets:

(*a*) the set of vowels;
(*b*) the set of odd numbers less than 10;
(*c*) the set of months beginning with the letter M;
(*d*) the set of whole numbers less than 20 which are prime numbers
(Is 1 a prime number?)

2.

(*a*) How many elements does the set of letters of our alphabet have?
(*b*) How many elements does the set of vowels of our alphabet have?

3.

(*a*) Write the members of the set of numbers less than 99 which are divisible by 9
(*b*) Write the set of numbers less than 99 in which the sum of the digits is 9
(*c*) Do the sets in (*a*) and (*b*) above have the same members?

4. List or tabulate the members of the following sets:

(*a*) the names of the Prime Ministers of the U.K. in the 1950s
(*b*) the set of symbols used in Roman numerals
(*c*) the set of the squares of all whole numbers between 0 and 10

5. State whether the following pairs of sets are EQUAL, EQUIVALENT or UNRELATED:

(*a*) {*a, p, r, t*} and {*r, a, p, t*}
(*b*) the set of prime numbers less than 10 and {2, 3, 5, 7}

(c) $\{a, b, c, d, e\}$ and $\{3, 7, 4, 8, 5\}$

(d) the set of odd numbers below 20 and the set of prime numbers below 20?

(e) {James, Peter, John} and {Sarah, Anne, Ruth, Jane}

(f) $\{9^3, 8^2, 16^3\}$ and $\{27^2, 64^2, 4^3\}$

(g) $\{1, 4, 6, 4, 1\}$ and {digits in 11^4}

(h) {letters of the word "parallel"} and {letters of the French word for "speak"}

(i) $\{1, 5, 10, 10, 5, 1\}$ and {digits in 11^5}

(j) the set of even natural numbers less than 20 and the set of odd natural numbers less than 20

6. Are the following statements true or false?

(a) $a \; \varepsilon \; \{a, e, i, o, u\}$

(b) $5 \; \varepsilon \; \{3, 9, 27, 81\}$

(c) $x \; \varepsilon \; \{p, q, r, s\}$

7. Are the following sets FINITE?

(a) {Possible games of chess}

(b) {Grains of sand on the Earth}

(c) {Numbers between 0 and 1}

(d) {Prime Numbers}

9. SUBSETS

Let us take the three Smith grandchildren as our set.

$$A = \{\text{Robert, Jill, William}\}$$

Robert is 12 years, Jill is 9 years, William is 3 years.
Together they represent a set.
The boys {Robert, William} are a SUBSET of A. symbol $\subset$.
What is the subset of girls?

$$\{\text{Jill}\} \subset \{\text{Robert, Jill, William}\}$$

The following is the total number of possible subsets:

{Robert, Jill}   {Robert}   {Robert, Jill, William}
{Robert, William} {Jill} ϕ
{Jill, William}   {William} (eight in all)

It will be seen that the null set is included.

Example

What is the set of Smith grandchildren under 2 years?

ϕ, the null set

Note that we have also included the original set as one of the subsets.

10. VENN DIAGRAMS

We can illustrate sets by using these diagrams as follows:

The symbol $\mathscr{E}$ represents the UNIVERSAL SET in each case.

Let $\mathscr{E}$ be the set of all children in a school.

Let A be the set of all children over 15 years.

Let B be the set of all children over 15 years who wear glasses.

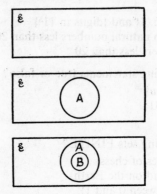

All members of A are also in $\mathscr{E}$

All members of B are included in A and in $\mathscr{E}$

11. DISJOINT SETS

Let $\mathscr{E}$ be the set of all children in a school

Let A be the set of all children over 15 years

Let C be the set of all children under 13 years

No members of A are included in C

But all of A and C are in $\mathscr{E}$

We say that A and C are disjoint in C.

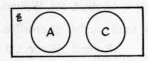

12. UNION

Let $A = \{a, b, c, d\}$

and $B = \{c, d, e, f\}$

Then the Union of A and $B = \{a, b, c, d, e, f\}$

The Union includes all members of both sets, not repeating any element.

We say "A union B" or "A cup B", written "$A \cup B$".

Using venn diagrams and the example above we get

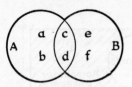

The left-hand circle represents set A and the right-hand circle set B. The union is outlined in black.

13. INTERSECTION

Let $A = \{a, b, c, d\}$
and $B = \{c, d, e, f\}$
Then the Intersection of A and $B = \{c, d\}$
The Intersection is composed of those elements which are common to the original sets.
We say "A intersection B" or "A cap B", written "$A \cap B$".
In Venn diagrams:

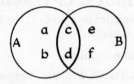

The intersection is outlined in black

Example

What is the Intersection of $\{a\ b\ c\}$ and $\{x\ y\ z\}$?
Answer ϕ, the Null set.
Or, in venn diagrams:

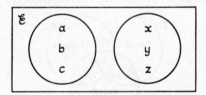

The circles do not overlap; the Intersection is the null set.

14. THE COMPLEMENT OF A SET

A soccer team has 11 members, 5 of whom comprise the forwards.
Let $A = \{$all the 5 forwards$\}$
Let $A' = \{$the remaining 6 players$\}$
Together they form the Universal set, $\mathscr{E}$, in this case the soccer team.

In venn form:

$$A \cup A' = \mathscr{E}$$

A set and its complement together form the universal set.

Example

Let Universal Set $= \{a, b, c, \ldots x, y, z\}$
If $A = \{a, e, i, o, u\}$

What is the Complement of A?

Answer

$A' = \{b, c, d, f, g, h, j, k, l, m, n, p, q, r, s, t, v, w, x, y, z\}$

15. EXAMPLES OF THE USE OF VENN DIAGRAMS

1. There are three societies in a school; the Film Society, the Jazz Club and the Printing Society.

The Film Society has 4 members

$$\{\text{Robin, David, William, Fergus}\} = F$$

The Jazz Club has 4 members

$$\{\text{Francis, Robin, Trog, William}\} = J$$

The Printing Society has 4 members

$$\{\text{Peter, Fergus, William, Trog}\} = P$$

Draw venn diagrams illustrating the membership.

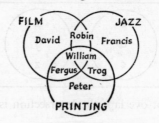

$$F \cup J = \{\text{David, Robin, William, Francis, Fergus, Trog}\}$$
$$F \cap J = \{\text{Robin, William}\}$$
$$J \cap P = \{\text{William, Trog}\}$$
$$J \cap P \cap F = \{\text{William}\}$$

2. In the VIth form of a school 21 boys take Maths, 17 take Physics and 10 take Chemistry. 12 boys take Maths and Physics,

6 take Maths and Chemistry, 5 take Physics and Chemistry. Two boys take all 3 subjects. (All the boys take at least one of the subjects.) How many boys are there in all?

Maths—21; Maths/Physics—12;

Physics—17; Maths/Chemistry—6;

Chemistry—10; Physics/Chemistry—5;

Maths/Physics/Chemistry—2.

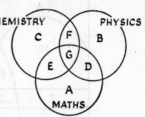

Let $n(X)$ = number of members of the set who take maths

Let $n(Y)$ = number of members of the set who take physics

Let $n(Z)$ = number of members of the set who take chemistry

(i) $n(X \cap Y \cap Z)$ = number who take all 3 subjects = 2 boys

Therefore $G = 2$

(ii) $n(Y \cap Z) - G$ = number who take physics and chemistry minus those who take all three = $5 - 2 = 3$ boys

Therefore $F = 3$

(iii) $n(X \cap Z) - G$ = number who take maths and chemistry minus those who take all three = $6 - 2 = 4$ boys

Therefore $E = 4$

(iv) $n(X \cap Y) - G = 12 - 2 = 10$

Therefore $D = 10$

(v) $n(Z) - [F + G + E] = 10 - [3 + 2 + 4] = 1$ $\therefore C = 1$

(vi) $n(Y) - [F + G + D] = 17 - [3 + 2 + 10] = 2$ $\therefore B = 2$

(vii) $n(X) - [D + G + E] = 21 - [10 + 2 + 4] = 5$ $\therefore A = 5$

$$n(X \cup Y \cup Z) = A + B + C + D + E + F + G$$
$$= 5 + 2 + 1 + 10 + 4 + 3 + 2$$
$$= 27$$

Therefore there are 27 boys in the VIth form.
The final answer looks like this:

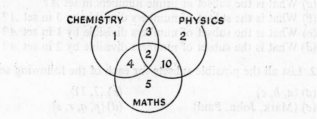

3. For problems involving the intersections of 4 sets the following diagram may be used.

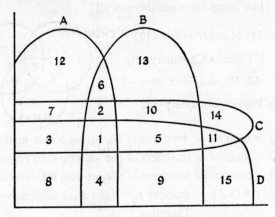

1. represents $A \cap B \cap C \cap D$
2. „ $A \cap B \cap C$
3. „ $A \cap C \cap D$
4. „ $A \cap B \cap D$
5. „ $B \cap C \cap D$
6. „ $A \cap B$
7. „ $A \cap C$
8. „ $A \cap D$
9. „ $B \cap D$
10. „ $B \cap C$
11. „ $C \cap D$
12. „   only A
13. „   „ B
14. „   „ C
15. „   „ D

EXERCISE No. 2

1. If $A = \{1, 3, 5, 7, 9\}$

(a) What is the subset of prime numbers in set A?
(b) What is the subset of numbers divisible by 3 in set A?
(c) What is the subset of numbers divisible by 1 in set A?
(d) What is the subset of numbers divisible by 2 in set A?

2. List all the possible subsets for each of the following sets:

(a) $\{a, b, c\}$ (b) $\{7, 11\}$
(c) $\{$Mark, John, Paul$\}$ (d) $\{p, q, r, s\}$

3. Name a subset of each of the following universal sets:

(*a*) the set of boys in a school
(*b*) the set of whole numbers greater than 3 and less than 30
(*c*) the set of four-sided figures
(*d*) the set of books in the school library

4. Show the relationships between the following sets with venn diagrams:

(*a*) {2, 4, 6, 8}   and {1, 3, 5, 7, 9}
(*b*) {1, 2, 3, 4, 5} and {4, 5, 6, 7, 8}
(*c*) {1, 2, 3, 4, 5} and {2, 3}
(*d*) {1, 2, 3, 4, 5} and {1, 2, 3, 4, 5}
(*e*) Members of Parliament, male M.Ps., female M.Ps.

5. Draw diagrams to show the relationships of the given pairs of sets:

(*a*) the set of odd numbers; the set of prime numbers
(*b*) the set of even numbers; the set of squares of odd numbers
(*c*) the set of numbers less than 100; the set of squares of whole numbers less than 10
(*d*) the set of numbers divisible by 2; the set of numbers divisible by 3

6. List the members of the union of each pair of sets:

(*a*) $A = \{a, b, c, d\}$; $B = \{b, d, f, h\}$
(*b*) $X = \{2, 4, 6, 8, 10\}$; $Y = \{3, 6, 9, 12\}$
(*c*) $A = \{$John, Peter, James$\}$
     $B = \{$Arthur, Paul, Peter$\}$
(*d*) $P = \{$Maths, Physics, Chemistry, Biology, Art$\}$
     $Q = \{$Biology, Chemistry, French, Latin$\}$

7. Draw and shade the areas that represent these unions:

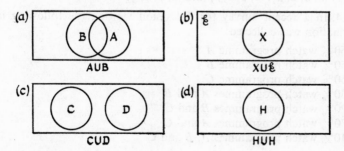

8. List the members of the intersection of each pair of sets:

(a) $\{a, b, c, d, e\}$ and $\{a, e, i, o, u\}$

(b) {James, Stephen, Paul, John} and {Adam, Stephen, Luke}

(c) The set of prime numbers less than 10; the set of odd numbers less than 10

9. Copy and shade the regions that represent the following inter-sections:

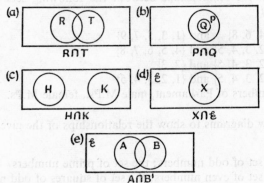

10. If the universal set is "all triangles", and R is the set of right-angled triangles, describe R'.

11. If $A = \{1, 2, 3, 4, 5\}$; $B = \{3, 5, 6, 7\}$; $C = \{2, 5, 7, 9\}$

Write down the members of

(a) $A \cup B$ (b) $A \cup C$ (c) $B \cap C$ (d) $A \cup (B \cap C)$

(e) $(A \cup B) \cap (A \cup C)$ (f) $(A \cup B) \cap C$ (g) $A \cap (B \cup C)$

(h) $A \cap (B \cap C)$ (i) $(A \cap B) \cap C$

12. If $n(X \cup Y) = 25$, $n(X \cap Y) = 5$, and $n(Y) = 14$, draw a venn diagram to illustrate these data, and find $n(X)$.

[O. and C. "O" level, July 1964]

13. Draw illustrated venn diagrams of:

(a) $\{a, b, c, d, e\}$ and $\{a, e, i, o, u\}$

(b) $\{a, b, c, d\}, \{b, d, e, f\}$ and $\{a, b, e, g\}$

14. In a recent survey for Television viewing the following in-formation was collected:

60% watch programme A
50% watch programme B
50% watch programme C
30% watch programmes A and B
20% watch programmes B and C
30% watch programmes A and C
10% watch programmes A, B and C

Find the percentage of people:

(a) who watch A and B but not C
(b) who watch just two programmes
(c) who do not watch any

15. $\mathscr{E} = \{1, 2, 3, 4, 5, 6, 7, 8, 9, 10\}$
   $X = \{2, 4, 6, 8\}$ $Z \cap Y = \{1, 3\}$
   $Y = \{1, 3, 5, 7\}$ $Z \cup Y = \{1, 2, 3, 5, 7, 9\}$

Use venn diagrams to find:

(a) the elements of Z
(b) $n(X) - n(Z \cap X)$ [$n(X)$ means "number of elements in X", etc.]
(c) $n(Z \cup X) - n((Z \cup Y)')$

16. What is the number of subsets in

(a) a set of 2 elements?
(b) a set of 3 elements?
(c) a set of 4 elements?
(d) a set of 5 elements?
(e) if n = number of elements in the set how many subsets has it?

17. One week the sports writers of three daily newspapers picked the following teams to win (the predictions are all for the same 4 matches):

League Division One

$A = \{$Arsenal, Spurs, Manchester United, Bolton$\}$
$B = \{$Arsenal, Everton, Stoke, Manchester United$\}$
$C = \{$Bolton, Arsenal, Fulham, Stoke$\}$

Nobody picked Ipswich to win.
Use venn diagrams to find the actual matches played.

18. Show the relationship between a straight line and a circle if the intersection set between the two is:

(a) the null set
(b) a set of one member
(c) a set of two members
(d) a set of three members

19. Draw a circle and a quadrilateral for which the intersection set is:

(a) a set of 2 points
(b) a set of 4 points
(c) a set of 6 points
(d) a set of 8 points

20. Given that $\mathscr{E} = \{1, 2, 3, 4, 5, 6, 7, 8, 9\}$
$A = \{1, 2, 3, 4\}$
$B = \{2, 4, 8\}$

Draw venn diagrams to find:

(a) $A \cup B$
(b) $A \cap B$
(c) $A' \cup B$
(d) $A \cap B'$

21. 30 girls were asked to write down what they normally drank out of tea (T), coffee (C) and lemonade (L). Every list contained at least one of them. 17 contained T, 15 contained C and 15 contained L. 7 contained both T and C, 6 both C and L and 8 both T and L. How many lists contained all three beverages?

22. 120 men were asked to say which of the following drinks they liked: beer (B), whisky (W) and cider (C). 40 said beer, 50 gave whisky and 60 said cider. 12 said they liked beer and cider but not whisky. 3 said they liked all three. 11 liked beer and whisky. 7 liked whisky and cider but not beer.

(a) Rewrite this information symbolically
(b) Complete a venn diagram showing the actual numbers in each of the 7 areas
(c) How many men liked none of these drinks?

23. 100 children were asked to say which toys they would like to be given, to be chosen from cars (C), dolls (D), bricks (B) and games (G).

The same number chose C, D and B; C, D and G; C, B and G. The number of children who chose C, D and B was one-third the number who chose D, B and G. 4 children chose C and D. The number who chose C and B; C and G; D and B was one-half the number who chose C, B and G. Twice the number who chose D and G was the same as three times the number who chose C, D and G. The same number chose B and G as chose C, B and G. The same number chose C only, G only and B only, the total for these 3 was 21. 2 chose D only. 8 chose all four. 5 children did not want any of the toys.

Complete a venn diagram showing the actual numbers of children.
[**Hint.** Let x = number who chose C, D and B.]

16. COMMUTATIVE LAW

(a) $5 + 4 = 4 + 5$

If we change the order of addition we do not alter the sum. It is known as the Commutative Law because the numbers commute or change places.

(b) $5 \times 4 = 4 \times 5$

This is also commutative; the change of place does not alter the product.

(c) $\frac{5}{4}$ does not equal $\frac{4}{5}$. So division is **not**, in general, commutative.

(d) We will now show that $A \cup B$ is the same as $B \cup A$

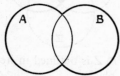 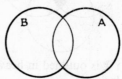

(in both cases the Union is outlined in black).
The results are the same. Therefore $A \cup B = B \cup A$

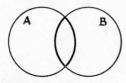 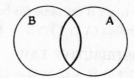

(e) Similarly, we show that $A \cap B = B \cap A$
(the intersection is outlined in black).
Therefore $A \cap B = B \cap A$

17. ASSOCIATIVE LAW

It is called Associative because the order of adding or associating any pair does not matter.

(a) $(2 + 4) + 6 = 2 + (4 + 6)$
(b) $(2 \times 4) \times 6 = 2 \times (4 \times 6)$
(c) We must show that $(X \cup Y) \cup Z = X \cup (Y \cup Z)$

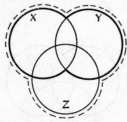 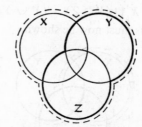

$X \cup Y$ is outlined in heavy $(Y \cup Z)$ is outlined in
   black   heavy black
$(X \cup Y) \cup Z$ is outlined in $X \cup (Y \cup Z)$ is outlined
   dotted lines   in dotted lines

The venn diagrams show that the result is the same.
Therefore $(X \cup Y) \cup Z = X \cup (Y \cup Z)$

(*d*) To show that $(X \cap Y) \cap Z = X \cap (Y \cap Z)$, we have:

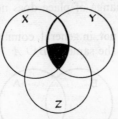 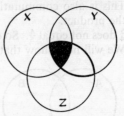

$X \cap Y$ is outlined in heavy black

$(X \cap Y) \cap Z$ is shaded black

$Y \cap Z$ is outlined in heavy black

$X \cap (Y \cap Z)$ is shaded black

The result is the same for both.

Therefore $(X \cap Y) \cap Z = X \cap (Y \cap Z)$

18. DISTRIBUTIVE LAW

(*a*) $2(4 + 5) = (2 \times 4) + (2 \times 5)$

The multiplier is distributed among the terms in the bracket, **but** multiplication cannot change places with addition.

Example

$7 + (3 \times 2)$ does not equal $(7 + 3) \times (7 + 2)$

Addition is **not** distributive with respect to multiplication.

N.B. Although multiplication is distributive with respect to addition and addition is **not** distributive with respect to multiplication it is found that union and intersection are distributive with respect to each other.

(*b*) $X \cup (Y \cap Z) = (X \cup Y) \cap (X \cup Z)$

This must now be shown.

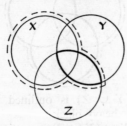 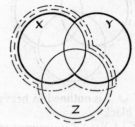

$Y \cap Z$ is in heavy black
$X \cup (Y \cap Z)$ is dotted

$X \cup Y$ is in heavy black
$X \cup Z$ is dotted
$(X \cup Y) \cap (X \cup Z)$ is shown thus — · — · — ·

(c) $X \cap (Y \cup Z) = (X \cap Y) \cup (X \cap Z)$

This is left to be done as an exercise by the reader.

19. (a) The equivalence between addition and union can be shown as follows:

$$a + 0 = a \qquad A \cup \phi = A$$

(b) The equivalence between multiplication and intersection can be shown thus:

$$a \times 1 = a \qquad A \cap \mathscr{E} = A$$
$$[\mathscr{E} = \text{Universal set}]$$

20. A summary of the laws governing union and intersection is as follows:

1. $A \cup A = A$
2. $A \cap A = A$
3. $A \cup B = B \cup A$
4. $A \cap B = B \cap A$
5. $A \cup (B \cup C) = (A \cup B) \cup C$
6. $A \cap (B \cap C) = (A \cap B) \cap C$
7. $A \cap (B \cup C) = (A \cap B) \cup (A \cap C)$
8. $A \cup (B \cap C) = (A \cup B) \cap (A \cup C)$
9. $A \cup \mathscr{E} = \mathscr{E}$
10. $A \cap \phi = \phi$
11. $A \cap \mathscr{E} = A$
12. $A \cup \phi = A$

EXERCISE No. 3

1. Verify the laws in Paragraph 20 by means of venn diagrams.

2. If $P \subset Q$ is $Q' \subset P'$?

3. If $A \subset B$, show that $A \cup B = B$; also show that $A \cap B = A$

4. $\mathscr{E} = \{1, 2, 3, 4, 5, 6, 7, 8, 9\}$
   $A = \{1, 2, 3, 4\}$
   $B = \{5, 6, 7, 8\}$
   $C = \{9\}$

Illustrate by using venn diagrams:

(a) $(A \cup B) \cap C$
(b) $A \cup (B \cap C)$
(c) $A \cup B'$
(d) $B \cap C'$

5. If $n(X)$, $n(Y)$ and $n(X \cap Y)$ are given, what is the formula for $n(X \cup Y)$?

6. Which of the following statements are: (a) always true; (b) sometimes true; (c) never true; (d) meaningless?

(i) $A \cup B = A + B$

(ii) $2A \cup A = 3A$

(iii) $A \cup B = B \cup A$

(iv) $A \cap B = A' \cup B'$

(v) $A \cup (B \cup C) = (A \cup B) \cup C$

(vi) $A \cap B = B \cap C$

7. Simplify:

(i) $A \cup A$

(ii) $A \cup \mathscr{E}$

(iii) $A \cap \phi$

(iv) $A \cup \phi$

(v) $A \cap A'$

(vi) $A \cup (A \cap B)$

(vii) $(A \cup B) \cup A'$

(viii) $(A \cap A') \cup B$

8. The sets A, B, C are defined as follows:

$$A = \{2, 3, 5\}; \ B = \{3, 5, 7\}; \ C = \{4, 5, 7, 11\}$$

(a) Write down the set $A \cap B$

(b) If $\pi(A)$ means the product of the elements of the set A, write down $\pi(A)$, $\pi(B)$ and $\pi(A \cap B)$, and state whether it is true or false that $\pi(A \cap B)$ is the highest factor common to $\pi(A)$ and $\pi(B)$

(c) Find out whether it is true that $\pi(A \cap C)$, is the highest factor common to $\pi(A)$ and $\pi(C)$, showing your working

(d) State conditions on the elements of two sets P and Q which ensure that $\pi(P \cap Q)$ is the highest factor common to $\pi(P)$ and $\pi(Q)$.

[O. and C. "O" level, July 1964]

9. Draw venn diagrams to illustrate

(a) $(A \cup B)' = A' \cap B'$

(b) $(A \cap B)' = A' \cup B'$ (De Morgan's Laws)

Chapter 2

PROBABILITY

1. A professional gambler, the Chevalier de Méré, asked Pascal (1623–62) for a solution to a problem he had in a game of chance. Briefly his problem was as follows: each of two players (at dice, say) requires a certain number of "points" to win the game, and if the game has to finish before this number is reached by either player, how should the stakes be divided between the players? In other words, what is the probability of each player winning the game, assuming that each player has an equal chance of winning a single point in the game?

Fermat (1601–65) and Pascal developed the fundamental principles of the mathematical theory of probability in correspondence during the year 1654.

The solution to the Chevalier's problem can be found by using common sense, but the mathematics of probability give a method for finding the number of possible cases without actually counting them.

For example, how many possible different hands each consisting of 3 aces and 3 other cards, none an ace, are there in a pack of 52 cards? Or, what is the chance of a six showing when a dice is thrown?

Pascal made great use of the arithmetical triangle

$$
\begin{array}{ccccccc}
 & & & 1 & & & \\
 & & 1 & & 1 & & \\
 & 1 & & 2 & & 1 & \\
 1 & & 3 & & 3 & & 1 \\
1 & & 4 & & 6 & & 4 & & 1 \\
\end{array}
$$

			1						
		1		1					1st row
	1		2		1				2nd row
1		3		3		1			3rd row
1	4		6		4		1		4th row
1	5	10		10		5		1	etc.

in which the numbers in any row after the first two are obtained from those in the preceding row by copying down the end ones and adding together the successive pairs of numbers, working from left to right. For example, in the 4th row $4 = 1 + 3$; $6 = 3 + 3$; $4 = 3 + 1$. The numbers in the nth row (after the first) are also the

27

coefficients in the expansion of $(1 + x)^n$ by the binomial theorem. For example:

$$(1 + x)^1 = 1 + x$$
$$(1 + x)^2 = 1 + 2x + x^2$$
$$(1 + x)^3 = 1 + 3x + 3x^2 + x^3$$
$$(1 + x)^4 = 1 + 4x + 6x^2 + 4x^3 + x^4$$

.

.   .

.   .

$$(1 + x)^n = 1 + nx + \frac{n(n - 1)x^2}{2!} + \frac{n(n - 1)(n - 2)x^3}{3!} + \cdots$$

[N.B. $2! = 2 \times 1$; $3! = 3 \times 2 \times 1$; $4! = 4 \times 3 \times 2 \times 1$, etc.]

Example

What are all the possible combinations of heads and tails that will occur when 3 pennies are tossed up together?

The possible results are as follows

1st Penny	2nd Penny	3rd Penny	
H	H	H	3 heads
H	H	T	
H	T	H	2 heads 1 tail
T	H	H	
T	T	H	
T	H	T	1 head 2 tails
H	T	T	
T	T	T	3 tails

There are 8 possible results, each being equally likely.
Hence there is:

a 1 in 8 chance of 3 heads
a 3 in 8 chance of 2 heads and 1 tail
a 3 in 8 chance of 1 head and 2 tails
a 1 in 8 chance of 3 tails

The numbers 1, 3, 3, 1 are the numbers in the 3rd row of the arithmetical triangle. This triangle is often called "PASCAL'S triangle", as he made use of it in the theory of mathematical probability; but it was known before his time.

EXERCISE No. 4

1. (a) Toss 2 pennies in the air and tabulate the results for 36 throws under the headings: 2 heads, 1 head and 1 tail, 2 tails.
   (b) Tabulate the possible results of throwing up 2 pennies in the air.
   (c) Compare the answers in questions (a) and (b).

2. (a) Toss 3 pennies in the air and tabulate the results for 36 throws under the headings: 3 heads, 2 heads and 1 tail, 1 head and 2 tails, 3 tails.
   (b) Compare the answers in (a) with the table on page 28.

The mathematical theory of probability founded by Pascal and Fermat is used today in, for example, modern physics, insurance, and in industry on pricing and quotations.

2. STATISTICAL PROBABILITY

How many fives are likely to be thrown in 36 trials with a die?

At each throw there are 6 possibilities, so in 6 throws we might expect to throw a five once. In 36 throws we might expect to get 6 fives. This does **not** mean, however, that in 36 throws we will in fact throw 6 fives; we might only get 3 fives or perhaps even 8 fives. The theoretical probability is 6 in 36 or 1 in 6

or $$p = \tfrac{1}{6}$$

However, if we throw the die many times, for example, 216 times, then we would expect to get **about** 36 fives, i.e.

$$p = \tfrac{36}{216} = \tfrac{1}{6}$$

The greater the number of throws, the nearer the actual probability would approach the theoretical value of $\tfrac{1}{6}$.

N.B. Provided that the die is not biased.

If you try this with a number of dice you may find that some give results closer to the theoretical value than others. With cheap dice this may mean that the dice are not evenly balanced.

Probability is defined as follows:

$$P = \frac{\text{Total number of times the expected event occurs}}{\text{Total number of trials}}$$

3. SCALE

The chance of an event occurring is given as number on the scale 0 to 1.

(*a*) Certainty

Suppose that today is Tuesday, then the probability that tomorrow is Wednesday is absolutely certain. We say that the Probability $= 1$

or $$P = 1$$

(*b*) Impossibility

Suppose that the present month is May, then the probability that the next month will be December is nil.
We say that the Probability $= 0$

or $$P = 0$$

(*c*) Between the limits $P = 0$ and $P = 1$

Suppose that you are asked to choose a card from 3 cards shown to you: ace of clubs, ace of spades and an ace of hearts.

Then the probability that you will choose an ace is certain, therefore $P = 1$.

The probability of choosing the queen of hearts is nil, therefore $P = 0$

However, the probability of choosing the ace of clubs is one chance in three, therefore $P = \frac{1}{3}$.

4. ADDITION LAW

Suppose a group of men is waiting at Paddington to catch a train; 40 are going to Reading, 60 to Didcot and 100 to Swindon. The whole group is the Universal Set and the problem may be represented in a venn diagram as follows:

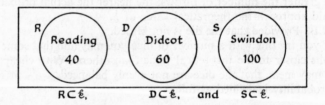

The subsets R, D and S are DISJOINT.

The total number of passengers $= n$(union of R, D and S) $= n(R \cup D \cup S) = 40 + 60 + 100 = 200$

The probability of asking someone in the group if he is going to

$$\text{Reading} = \frac{\text{Number going to Reading}}{\text{Total number of passengers}} = \frac{40}{200}$$

or
$$p\,(\text{Reading}) = \frac{1}{5}$$

[N.B. Each person has an equal chance of being asked.]
Similarly,

$$p\,(\text{Didcot}) = \frac{\text{Number going to Didcot}}{\text{Total number of passengers}} = \frac{60}{200}$$

or
$$p\,(\text{Didcot}) = \frac{3}{10}$$

and
$$p\,(\text{Swindon}) = \frac{100}{200} = \frac{1}{2}$$

The venn diagram illustrating the probabilities is as follows:

Adding the probabilities together we have

$$p(R) + p(D) + p(S) = \frac{1}{5} + \frac{3}{10} + \frac{1}{2} = \frac{2+3+5}{10} = \frac{10}{10} = 1$$

which means that the chance of asking a man if he is going to Reading, Didcot, or Swindon is 1, i.e. he must be going to one of the three places.

What is the probability of speaking to a man going to either Reading or Didcot?

$$p(R \cup D) = p(R) + p(D) = \frac{1}{5} + \frac{3}{10} = \frac{2+3}{10} = \frac{5}{10} = \frac{1}{2}$$

What is the probability of speaking to a man going to either Reading or Swindon?

$$p(R \cup S) = p(R) + p(S) = \frac{1}{5} + \frac{1}{2} = \frac{2+5}{10} = \frac{7}{10}$$

The Addition Law can be summed up as follows:

The probability that an event will occur in one of several possible ways = The sum of the probabilities of each event occurring, where the events are mutually exclusive.

N.B. The addition law is used when the events are independent of each other. This will, I hope, become clearer when we consider the Multiplication Law.

5. MULTIPLICATION LAW

Suppose a group of 30 scientists from different countries contains 10 who speak English and 6 who speak Russian. This can be represented in a venn diagram as follows:

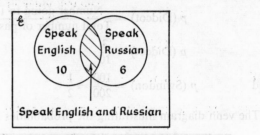

The Universal Set contains 30 scientists,

$$E \subset \mathscr{E} \text{ and has 10 elements}$$
$$R \subset \mathscr{E} \text{ and has 6 elements}$$

(a) What is the probability of meeting a scientist who speaks English?

$$p(E) = \frac{\text{Number who speak English}}{\text{Total number in Group}} = \frac{10}{30} = \frac{1}{3}$$

(b) What is the probability of meeting a scientist who speaks Russian?

$$p(R) = \frac{\text{Number who speak Russian}}{\text{Total number in Group}} = \frac{6}{30} = \frac{1}{5}$$

The probabilities can be represented in a venn diagram as follows:

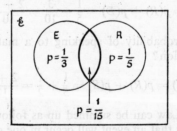

(c) What is the probability of meeting a scientist who can speak both Russian and English?

A third of the group speaks English, therefore if ability to speak Russian is independent of the ability to speak English it is reasonable to suppose that a third of the Russian speakers will speak English. Since the Russian speakers form a fifth of the group, the fraction of the group speaking both languages is a third of a fifth,

e.g.

$$\frac{1}{3} \times \frac{1}{5} = \frac{1}{15}$$

This is represented in the diagram by the intersection of E and R,

i.e. $E \cap R$

(outlined in heavy black)

$$p(E \cap R) = p(E) \times p(R)$$

$$= \frac{1}{3} \times \frac{1}{5} = \frac{1}{15}$$

As there are 30 in the Universal Set and

$$p(E \cap R) = \frac{1}{15}$$

then there are probably 2 who speak English and Russian.

(d) What is the probability of meeting a scientist who speaks neither language?

The number who speak English $= n(E) = 10$

The number who speak Russian $= n(R) = 6$

The number who speak English and Russian $= n(E \cap R) = 2$ (probably).

implies $n(E \cup R) = 10 + 6 - 2 = 14$

implies $n(E \cup R)' = 30 - 14 = 16$

$n(E \cup R)' =$ probable number who do not speak English or Russian

Hence the probability of meeting a scientist who speaks neither language $= \dfrac{16}{30} = \dfrac{8}{15}$.

The multiplication law can be summed up as follows:

The probability of several events occurring to the same elements of a set is obtained by multiplying together the individual probabilities.

$$P = p_1 \times p_2 \times p_3, \text{ etc.}$$

C

Here is another example.

In a group of 200 people, 40 like fish, 50 like meat and 20 like eggs. Find the probable number of people who like (*a*) fish and meat, (*b*) meat and eggs, (*c*) fish, meat and eggs.

The venn diagram is as follows:

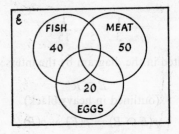

The probabilities are obtained as follows:

(i) People who like fish $P(F) = \dfrac{40}{200} = \dfrac{1}{5}$

(ii) People who like meat $P(M) = \dfrac{50}{200} = \dfrac{1}{4}$

(iii) People who like eggs $P(E) = \dfrac{20}{200} = \dfrac{1}{10}$

These probabilities can be illustrated in a venn diagram, as follows:

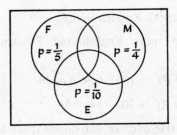

(*a*) The probability that a person likes fish and meat is

$$p(F \cap M) = \frac{1}{5} \times \frac{1}{4} = \frac{1}{20}$$

hence the probable number of people who like fish and meat

$= \dfrac{1}{20} \times 200$ people $= 10$ people

(b) The probability that a person likes meat and eggs is

$$p(M \cap E) = \frac{1}{4} \times \frac{1}{10} = \frac{1}{40}$$

hence the probable number of people who like meat and eggs
$$= \frac{1}{40} \times 200 \text{ people} = 5 \text{ people}$$

(c) The probability that a person likes fish, meat and eggs is

$$p(F \cap M \cap E) = \frac{1}{5} \times \frac{1}{4} \times \frac{1}{10} = \frac{1}{200}$$

hence the probable number of people who like fish, meat and
eggs $= \frac{1}{200} \times 200 \text{ people} = 1 \text{ person}$

EXERCISE No. 5

1. What is the chance of an even number appearing on one throw of a 6-sided die?

2. What is the chance of selecting a vowel, first time, from TO-NIGHT?

3. What is the chance of drawing in one trial, from a pack of 52 cards: (a) an ace; (b) the Queen of spades; (c) any ace, King or Queen?

4. A bag contains 7 black balls, 12 white balls and 11 red balls. What is the chance of drawing: (a) a white ball; (b) either a black or red ball; (c) either a white or red ball?

5. Of a group of 25 children, 9 have blue eyes and 16 have brown eyes. If 2 children are selected from the group, what is the probability that both will have: (a) blue eyes; (b) brown eyes?

6. If 3 cards are chosen from a pack of cards what is the probability that: (a) all three will be clubs; (b) 2 will be hearts and the third a spade?

7. In a local election 40% of the electorate exercised their right to vote. Mr Smith received 55% of the votes cast and Mr Brown received 45%. What is the probability that an elector: (a) voted; (b) voted for Mr Smith?

8. In a certain country it is said that a driver has an accident every 200,000 miles. If a driver expects to drive 8,000 miles next year, what is the probability that he will not have an accident?

9. What is the probability of throwing in 3 successive throws of a die a two, a three and a four?

10. In a group of tourists, 40 are English, 20 are Irish, 10 are

French, 15 are American, 5 are German, 7 are Russian and 3 are Chinese. What are the probabilities of speaking to:

(a) Someone who is Irish
(b) Someone who is either Irish or American
(c) Someone who is **not** Russian
(d) Someone who is either English or French or German
(e) Someone who is **not** Chinese nor Russian?

11. In a group of children 8 boys and 6 girls wear glasses, 22 boys and 14 girls do not. What is the chance of choosing, at random from the whole group:

(a) One child who wears glasses
(b) One boy who wears glasses
(c) Two boys, both of whom wear glasses
(d) Two boys followed by 1 girl, none of whom wears glasses?

12. Two people are each asked to write down a number less than 10 (0 not allowed). What is the chance that: (i) both are less than 5; (ii) they are the same; (iii) they add up to 5?

13. If a die is thrown, what is the probability of not getting a three in the first 3 throws?

14. Of a group of 200 children, 60 learn French, 5 learn Latin, 120 learn Algebra and 150 learn English. Find the probabilities that:

(a) a child learns French or Latin
(b) a child learns Latin, Algebra and English
(c) a child learns French, Latin, Algebra and English
(d) a child does not learn any of these subjects

15. Of a batch of 2,000 new cars, 25 had steering trouble, 40 had electrical faults and 120 had faulty gear-boxes. What is the probability of a customer buying a car:

(a) with a non-electrical fault
(b) having all three defects
(c) without one of the defects?

16. A sample of 500 men is taken. 400 of them earn less than £1,000 a year. Of the 300 who are married, 20 have 1 child, 80 have 2 children and 15 have 3 children. What are the probabilities that:

(a) a man is married with 2 children and earns less than £1,000 p.a.
(b) a man is single and earns more than £1,000 p.a.
(c) Find the probable number of men in (a) and (b)?

17. From a group of 5 boys and 4 girls, 2 children are selected at random. What is the probability that:

(a) the first will be a boy and the second a girl
(b) they are both girls?

18. A bicycle manufacturer made a batch of 2,000 tricycles, all of which were sold. If 50 had brake defects, 40 had weak links in the chain and 20 had perished inner tubes, what is the chance of someone buying:

(*a*) a tricycle without a weak link in the chain
(*b*) a tricycle with **none** of these defects?

19. There are 200 boys in a school. 120 are very keen on hockey, 70 are very keen on football. What is the probability of a boy being very keen on hockey and football?

20. Three pennies are tossed up. What is the chance that:

(*a*) the three coins will turn up all heads
(*b*) the three coins will turn up two heads and one tail?

21. Among a group of 40 barbarians 8 shave their heads, 16 pierce their noses, 2 wear no clothes, 32 like music, 20 practise polygamy and 4 eat their wives. What is the chance of meeting a barbarian who

(*a*) does not shave his head
(*b*) does wear clothes and practises polygamy?

Chapter 3

NUMBER

1. A symbol is often used when one wishes to refer to an object or thing. When the symbol is used one may think of the object or thing to which it refers, or if one did not know of this association one might think just of the symbol itself. There are, then, two distinct ways of looking at a symbol. For example, Barclays Bank use as their symbol

When one sees this sign or symbol one either:

(*a*) thinks of BARCLAYS BANK

or

(*b*) thinks of the symbol, i.e. the EAGLE itself

When one is talking about a NUMBER, then the symbol that stands for the number is called a NUMERAL.

Numbers have been represented by people in the past in many ways. For example, the number five was represented by

The Egyptians thus: | | |
                                      | |

The Babylonians thus: v v v
                                     v v

The Romans thus: V

The Ionian Greeks thus: ε

All these symbols can be thought of as referring either

(*a*) to the number five

or

(*b*) to the actual symbols themselves

The numerals used today have been devised from the Hindu–Arabic system.

1   17   109   2070

As children, when we were faced with a set of objects we would see how many there were by deliberately counting them one at a time. Hence the natural

ONE to ONE

matching of the set of objects with the set of counting numbers led us to the appropriate numeral.

$$\{ \quad 1 \qquad\qquad 2 \qquad\qquad 3 \qquad \}$$

In this case: 3

EXERCISE No. 6

1. Find out what symbols have been used to represent one, five, ten, hundred, 1,000 by:

(a) the Ancient Egyptians
(b) the Babylonians
(c) the Romans
(d) the Ionian Greeks

2. Find out what the numerals 1, 2, 3, 4, 5, 6, 7, 8, 9 looked like about A.D. 1000.

3. Find the product of VII and XI (Roman symbols).

4. Can you think of some of the reasons why you would not like to do arithmetic using Roman symbols?

2. The number of objects in a set is known as the CARDINAL number of that set.

e.g.		No. of Eyes	Cardinal No. 2
		No. of legs	3
		No. of prongs	4

3. The numerals with which we count (1, 2, 3, . . . etc.) are an infinite set, that is, there is no end to the set. We cannot count zero, so zero is not a counting number.

We can add these numerals

$$3 + 4 = 7$$

and for any pair there is a numeral which is their sum.

4. The counting numbers we call the NATURAL numbers, zero is excluded. Sometimes we refer to the "whole" numbers, and then we mean the natural numbers and ZERO.

5. In mathematics many kinds of operations are possible. Any given operation and its characteristics are determined by the actual assumptions chosen to define that operation.

The foundations of elementary mathematics are built upon two operations,

ADDITION and MULTIPLICATION

These are assumed to be BINARY OPERATIONS. A binary operation is performed when we carry out **one** operation on **two** elements (a and b) of a given set and produce a unique element (c) which is also an element of the same set.

Example 1

If S represents the set of natural numbers, then

$$3 + 4 = 7$$

is a binary operation, since we have carried out the operation of ADDITION on two natural numbers 3 and 4 and produced 7, which belongs to the set of natural numbers.

Example 2

If a and b belong to the set of natural numbers, then their sum, $(a + b) = c$, is a binary operation, as c is a member of the set of natural numbers.

Example 3

If S represents one set of natural numbers, then

$$3 \times 4 = 12$$

is a binary operation, since we have carried out the operation of multiplication on 2 natural numbers 3 and 4 and produced 12, which belongs to the set of natural numbers.

Example 4

If a and b belong to the set of natural numbers, then their product $(a \times b) = d$ is a binary operation, as d is a member of the set of natural numbers.

Example 5

Example of an operation that is **not** Binary,

$$5 - 8 = -3$$

The set of natural numbers includes five and eight, but does **not** have minus three as a member.

Therefore subtraction is **not** a binary operation in the set of natural numbers.

[N.B. A binary operation produces an element which is a member of the set containing the elements being operated upon.]

EXERCISE No. 7

1. Is division a binary operation in the set of natural numbers?

2. Find the value of

(a) $(3 + 5) \times 4$ (b) $3 + (5 \times 4)$

(c) $(3 \times 5) + 4$ (d) $3 \times (5 + 4)$

3. If p and q are members of the set of natural numbers, which of the following always represent a natural number?

(a) $p + q$ (b) $p - q$

(c) pq (d) $\dfrac{p}{q}$

4. In the parts of Question 3 which do not always represent a natural number, what condition must be satisfied by p and q in order that these expressions will always represent natural numbers?

6. We assume that the natural numbers have certain properties, listed below:

(a) $a + b = c$

Example

$$3 + 5 = 8$$

(b) $xy = z$

Example

$$2 \times 3 = 6$$

(c) $x + y = y + x$

Example

$$2 + 3 = 3 + 2 \text{ (addition is commutative)}$$

(d) $x + (y + z) = (x + y) + z$ (addition is associative)

(e) $xy = yx$

Example

　　3 × 4 = 4 × 3 (multiplication is commutative)

(f) x(yz) = (xy)z (multiplication is associative)

(g) x(y + z) = xy + xz (multiplication is distributive with respect to addition)

(h) There is a unity element such that

$$1 \times x = x \times 1 = x$$

7. We have seen that Subtraction is not a Binary operation.

e.g. 3 − 5 does not produce a natural number.

But if we consider 3 − 5 = −2 as 3 + 2 = 5, (3 − 5) means that number which when added to 5 gives 3.

We introduce the number ZERO and POSITIVE and NEGATIVE INTEGERS.

If we draw a straight horizontal line and mark on it zero, then the positive integers are marked off on the right and the negative integers on the left.

```
                         Zero
                          |
·······-5  -4  -3  -2  -1  0  1  2  3  4  5 ········
      Negative integers   |   Positive integers
```

Notice that the numerals (counting numbers) are included in the set of integers.

8. If we add zero to any integer it has no effect,

e.g. 4 + 0 = 4

However, if we multiply 4 by zero the product is zero,

e.g. 4 × 0 = 0

But when we divide 4 by 0 the result is not defined,

e.g. $\frac{4}{0} = ?$

If we have a very small number instead of 0, then,

$$4 \div \frac{1}{1,000,000} = 4 \times 1,000,000 = 4 \text{ million}$$

9. In paragraph 7 we saw that the integers could be represented by points on a line. The next question to be answered is "what happens between 2 consecutive integers?"

e.g. $2\frac{1}{2}$ or $\frac{5}{2}$ is midway between 2 and 3

A number like $\frac{5}{2}$ we call a RATIONAL number and define it.
A rational number is obtained by dividing an integer by any other integer, neither of them zero.

Example 1   **Example 2**

$$\frac{-3}{-2} = +\frac{3}{2} \qquad\qquad \frac{-6}{+2} = -3$$

Example 1 means how many minus twos are there in the integer minus three. There are one and one half.
Example 2 means how many $(+2)$s are there in -6. There are -3.

Let us now redraw the diagram in paragraph 7 to include some of the rational numbers.

Consider the rational numbers $\frac{5}{4}$ and $\frac{3}{2}$ $(= \frac{6}{4})$
Between them is the rational number $\frac{11}{8}$, obtained thus:

$$\frac{5}{4} = \frac{10}{8} \text{ and } \frac{3}{2} = \frac{12}{8} \qquad \frac{11}{8} \text{ lies between } \frac{10}{8} \text{ and } \frac{12}{8}$$

Between $\frac{10}{8}$ and $\frac{11}{8}$ is another rational number $\frac{21}{16}$ because $\frac{10}{8} = \frac{20}{16}$ and $\frac{11}{8} = \frac{22}{16}$, hence $\frac{21}{16}$ lies between $\frac{20}{16}$ and $\frac{22}{16}$.
In general, between any 2 rational numbers there always exists another rational number.*

10. Between the integers 1 and 2 there are many rational numbers. Now consider the square root of 2, $(\sqrt{2})$. Is this a rational number?
    The Greek mathematician Pythagoras showed that it is not rational.
    He supposed that $\sqrt{2}$ was rational and could be written $\frac{x}{y}$, where x and y are integers with no common factor,

i.e. $$\sqrt{2} = \frac{x}{y}$$

therefore $2 = \dfrac{x^2}{y^2}$ therefore $2y^2 = x^2$

If y is odd, then y^2 is odd, but $2y^2$ must therefore be even, therefore x^2 is even.
    If y is even, then y^2 is even, therefore $2y^2$ is even, therefore again x^2 is even.

* Or: If $\dfrac{a}{b} < \dfrac{e}{f}$, then $\dfrac{a}{b} < \dfrac{a+e}{b+f} < \dfrac{e}{f}$ where a,b,e,f are rational.

In either event x^2 is even, therefore x is even.

As x is even, then there is a positive integer K such that

$$2K = x$$

Substituting in $2y^2 = x^2$ we have

$$2y^2 = 4K^2$$

therefore 　　　　　　　　$y^2 = 2K^2$

As before, if K is odd or even, $2K^2$ must be even,

therefore 　　　　　　　y^2 is even

therefore 　　　　　　　　y is even

Pythagoras thus showed that x and y are both even and must therefore have a common factor **but** he started by assuming that x and y did **not** have a common factor.

Therefore it is not true that

$$\sqrt{2} = \frac{x}{y}$$

There is therefore no rational number which, when squared, gives 2.

We call numbers like this

IRRATIONAL numbers

Example

$$\sqrt{2}, \ \sqrt{3}, \ \sqrt{5}, \ \sqrt{6}, \text{ etc.}$$

It can be shown that all these are irrational in a similar way as $\sqrt{2}$ was shown to be irrational.

In general, if

$$x = \sqrt[n]{y}$$

(x equals the nth root of y)

where 　　$x \times x \times x \times x \times x \times x \times x \ (n \text{ times}) = y$

and if there does not exist a rational number x for given y then $\sqrt[n]{y}$ is irrational.

Example

$$\sqrt[5]{7} = y \text{ means } y \times y \times y \times y \times y = 7$$

11. REAL NUMBERS

Other examples of irrational numbers (i.e. numbers which cannot be obtained exactly) are:

(a) π

　　Circumference of circle $= 2\pi r$ 　　　　Area of circle $= \pi r^2$

The exact value of π cannot be determined, it is an irrational number. When an approximation for π is used, such as $\frac{22}{7}$ or $3 \cdot 142$, then the approximations are rational.

(b) e

The base of NATURAL logarithms.

$$e = 1 + 1 + \frac{1}{2!} + \frac{1}{3!} + \frac{1}{4!} + \frac{1}{5!} + \dots$$

[Where $2! = 1 \times 2$; $3! = 3 \times 2 \times 1$; $4! = 4 \times 3 \times 2 \times 1$; etc., e is irrational, but the approximate value, $2 \cdot 718$, is rational.]

Hence:

(*a*) Rational Numbers are a subset of Real Numbers
(*b*) Irrational Numbers are a subset of Real Numbers

12. IMAGINARY NUMBERS

$\sqrt{3}$ is irrational but what happens if we have $\sqrt{-3}$ or $\sqrt{-2}$ or $\sqrt{-1}$, etc?

$\begin{cases} \text{Question: Solve } x^2 = -1 \\ \text{What number multiplied by itself gives a product of } -1? \end{cases}$

Certainly there is no real number, e.g. try $x = 1$, then $x^2 = +1$.

Now try $x = -1$, then $x^2 = -1 \times -1 = +1$.

By taking the square root of both sides of the original equation we get

$$x = \pm \sqrt{-1}$$

The $\sqrt{-1}$ is called an IMAGINARY number because it does not have a Real number answer.

However, let us call $+ \sqrt{-1}$ the letter i, i.e. $i = + \sqrt{-1}$

Then $\qquad x = i$ or $x = -i$ $\qquad$ N.B. $\sqrt{-1} \times \sqrt{-1} = i^2$

Example

Solve $\qquad\qquad x^2 = -5$

therefore $\qquad\qquad x^2 = (+5) \times (-1)$

then $\qquad\qquad x = \pm \sqrt{+5} \times \sqrt{-1}$

$\qquad\qquad\qquad = \pm \sqrt{5} \times i$

$\qquad\qquad\qquad x = \pm i\sqrt{5}$

The idea of an imaginary number is an abstract idea but surely no more abstract than the idea of a number itself.

13. GEOMETRICAL REPRESENTATION

On an x, y graph let the y-axis be counted in units of $+i$ and $-i$. Let the x-axis be real numbers.

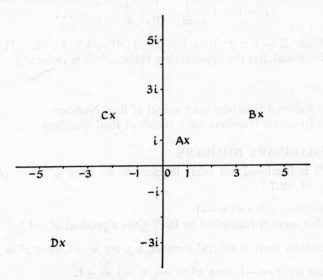

Point A has co-ordinates $x = 1$, $y = i$

Point B has co-ordinates $x = 4$, $y = 2i$

Point C has co-ordinates $x = -2$, $y = 2i$

Point D has co-ordinates $x = -4$, $y = -3i$

14. COMPLEX NUMBERS

In the graph just drawn the point A can be written

$$x = 1, y = i$$

or

$$(1 + i)$$

where it is understood that the REAL part is measured along the x-axis and the IMAGINARY part along the y-axis.

Hence point B can be written $4 + 2i$

and point C can be written $-2 + 2i$

and point D can be written $-4 - 3i$

Numbers such as these are called COMPLEX numbers, and consist of REAL and IMAGINARY parts.

In general,

> $(a + ib)$ represents all complex numbers

where a is the Real part

> and ib the Imaginary part ["b" is never Imaginary.]

N.B. a and b are both real numbers, and b becomes Imaginary when multiplied by i.

15.

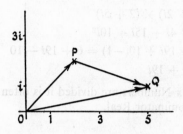

The arrow OP represents the complex number $2 + 2i$.

The arrow PQ represents 3 units on the x-axis and $-i$ on the y-axis.

Hence it represents the complex number $3 - i$.

Now consider the arrow OQ. By observation and counting it can be seen to be $5 + i$.

But

$$\left. \begin{array}{l} OP = 2 + 2i \\ PQ = 3 - i \\ \text{and } OQ = 5 + i \end{array} \right\}$$ Notice that OQ is obtained by adding the Real parts of OP and PQ and the Imaginary parts of OP and PQ separately

The lines represented by arrows are called VECTORS.
A vector quantity has magnitude and direction.

Addition of Complex Numbers

$$a + ib$$
$$c + id$$

Add $\qquad (a + c) + i(b + d)$

Example

$$(5 - 4i) + (-3 + 2i)$$
$$= 2 - 2i$$

Multiplication of Complex Numbers

First consider $(i \times i)$

The answer $= i^2$, but $\sqrt{-1} = i$

therefore $\qquad\qquad\qquad\qquad i^2 = -1$

hence $\qquad\qquad\qquad i^3 = -i$ and $i^4 = +1$

Example

$$(3 + 2i) \times (2 + 5i)$$
$$= 6 + 4i + 15i + 10i^2$$
$$= 6 + 19i + 10(-1) = 6 + 19i - 10$$
$$= -4 + 19i$$

If two Complex Numbers are divided it is often more convenient to make the denominator Real.

Example

$$\frac{2 + 3i}{3 - 2i}$$

In elementary algebra

$$a^2 - b^2 = (a + b)(a - b)$$

and we use this in solving our problem.

Take the bottom line $(3 - 2i)$ and multiply by the same complex number but with a change of sign of the 2nd term, i.e. $(3 + 2i)$.

Then $\qquad\qquad (3 - 2i) \times (3 + 2i)$
$$= 9 - 4i^2 = 9 - (-4) = 13$$

To return to the problem

$$\frac{2 + 3i}{3 - 2i}$$

If we multiply the bottom line by $(3 + 2i)$, then we must also multiply the top line by the same quantity so as not to alter the original fraction.

$$\frac{2 + 3i}{3 - 2i} \times \frac{(3 + 2i)}{(3 + 2i)}$$

$$= \frac{6 + 9i + 4i + 6i^2}{13} = \frac{6 + 13i + (-6)}{13}$$

$$= \frac{0 + 13i}{13} = \frac{13i}{13} = i$$

EXERCISE No. 8

1. What are the cardinal numbers of the following sets:

(a) $\{a\ b\ c\}$
(b) {members of a cricket team}
(c) $\{P\ Q\ R\ S\ T\}$
(d) {set of symbols used by the Romans for counting}?

2. Explain the difference between "number" and "numeral".

3. Give two meanings of the symbol used by the "Shell" Petroleum Company.

4. What assumptions justify the following statements:

(a) $(a + b)$ is a natural number [a and b are natural numbers]
(b) $2 + 5 = 5 + 2$
(c) $(6 + 3) + 2 = 6 + (3 + 2)$
(d) $(2 \times 3) \times 4 = 2 \times (3 \times 4)$
(e) $6 \times 7 = 7 \times 6$
(f) $(2 + 5) \times 3 = 3 \times (2 + 5)$
(g) $3(2 + 4) = 3 \times 2 + 3 \times 4$?

5. Prove that the sum of two positive integers is always a positive integer.

6. Prove that the sum of two negative integers is always a negative integer.

7. Find the fallacy in the following:

$$p = q \qquad \therefore\ p^2 = pq \qquad \therefore\ p^2 - q^2 = pq - q^2$$
$$\therefore\ (p - q)(p + q) = q(p - q) \qquad \therefore\ p + q = q$$
$$\therefore\ 2q = q \qquad\qquad \therefore\ 2 = 1$$

8. Which is the greater of the pairs of rational numbers:

(a) $\frac{7}{17}$ or $\frac{11}{29}$
(b) $\frac{3}{13}$ or $\frac{2}{7}$
(c) $\frac{19}{11}$ or $\frac{9}{5}$
(d) $\frac{5}{13}$ or $\frac{7}{23}$?

9. Find a Rational number between each of the following pairs of Rational numbers:

(a) $\frac{1}{3}$ and $\frac{1}{2}$
(b) $\frac{4}{9}$ and $\frac{3}{7}$
(c) $\frac{10}{7}$ and $\frac{7}{5}$
(d) $\frac{17}{23}$ and $\frac{3}{4}$

10. Prove that $\sqrt{3}$ is irrational
[**Hint.** Show that 3 is not a common factor.]

11. Express each of the following as a recurring decimal:

(a) $\frac{11}{3}$ (b) $\frac{4}{9}$ (c) $\frac{7}{6}$ (d) $\frac{2}{7}$

D

12. What rational numbers are represented by

(a) 0·125 (b) 0·7777 . . .
(c) 0·27272727 . . . (d) 0·1428571428571 . . .

13. Simplify

(a) $\sqrt{-25}$ (b) $\sqrt{-32}$ (c) $-\sqrt{-36}$
(d) $2\sqrt{-98}$ (e) $-3i^4$ (f) i^5
(g) $2i^8$ (h) $-4i^6$ (i) $7i^3$

14. Find, in their simplest forms, the following products:

(a) $\sqrt{-4} \times \sqrt{-25}$ (b) $\sqrt{-15} \times \sqrt{-45}$
(c) $i \times 3i^3 \times 2i^2$ (d) $\sqrt{-9} \times \sqrt{-8} \times \sqrt{-2}$

15. Find the sums of the following complex numbers:

(a) $(3 + 4i) + (7 + 2i)$ (b) $(1 + 2i) + (5 + 8i)$
(c) $(4 + i) + (3 - 2i)$ (d) $(-3 + 5i) + (5 - 3i)$
(e) $(-\frac{3}{2} + 6i) + (2 - \frac{15}{2}i)$ (f) $(0 + i) + (-1 - i)$

16. Illustrate, on graph paper, the answers obtained in Question 15.

17. Find the products of the following:

(a) $(2 - i)(1 + i)$ (b) $(3 - i)(3 + i)$
(c) $(-4 - i)(1 + i)$ (d) $(0 + i)(0 - i)$
(e) $(1 + i)^2$ (f) $(3 - 2i)(3 + 2i)$

18. Simplify the following:

(a) $\dfrac{2}{1 - i}$ (b) $\dfrac{1 - i}{1 + i}$ (c) $\dfrac{3}{2 - 3i}$

(d) $\dfrac{1 - 2i}{1 + 2i}$ (e) $\dfrac{1}{i}$ (f) $\dfrac{1}{i - 1}$

(g) $\dfrac{1}{\sqrt{2} - i}$ (h) $\dfrac{1}{2 + i\sqrt{3}}$ (i) $\dfrac{1}{i - \sqrt{3}}$

19. Solve for x in the following:

(a) $x^2 - 3 = 0$ (b) $x^2 - 4 = 0$ (c) $x^2 + 3 = 0$
(d) $x^2 + 4 = 0$ (e) $x^2 - 2x + 1 = 0$ (f) $x^2 + x + 1 = 0$

16. "SCALE OF TEN" OR DENARY SYSTEM

There are ten symbols 0, 1, 2, 3, 4, 5, 6, 7, 8, 9. In forming a number the position of a symbol is important. For example, 38,765 is made up of three ten-thousands, eight thousands, seven hundreds, six tens and five units.

$$10,000 = 10^4 \quad (10 \times 10 \times 10 \times 10)$$
$$1,000 = 10^3 \quad (10 \times 10 \times 10)$$
$$100 = 10^2 \quad (10 \times 10)$$
$$10 = 10^1 \quad (10)$$
$$1 = 10^0 \quad \text{(By mathematical convention any number raised to the power of zero} = \text{one)}$$

hence

$$38,765 = (3 \times 10^4) + (8 \times 10^3) + (7 \times 10^2) + (6 \times 10^1)$$
$$+ (5 \times 10^0)$$

However other scales are in constant use, for example:

(1) 12 pence   = 1 shilling (Duodecimal)

(2) 16 ounces   = 1 pound (Scale of 16)

(3) 3 feet   = 1 yard (Scale of 3)

(4) 14 pounds   = 1 stone (Scale of 14)

(5) 2 halfpennies = 1 penny (Scale of 2, known as the Binary scale)

17. BINARY SCALE

With the introduction, some years ago, of the electronic computer, came an increased interest in the BINARY SCALE, because its two-symbol scale is particularly suited to these machines.

Modern electronic computers are equipped with batteries of valves or other two-state devices such as transistors or magnetic cores, with which the arithmetic is done.

One characteristic of electrical elements is that each one may be either ON or OFF, i.e. each can be in one of two states.

The binary scale is the obvious way of representing numbers by means of the state of electrical elements.

The following lamps are connected together

and this represents the number five on the binary scale, as will be explained later.

Computers work extremely quickly and can be designed to work with words as well as numbers by using LOGIC.

The two symbols on the binary scale are

1 and 0

On the denary scale powers of 10 are used
On the binary scale powers of 2 are used
e.g.

$$2^4 = 2 \times 2 \times 2 \times 2 = (16 \text{ on denary scale})$$
$$2^3 = 2 \times 2 \times 2 \qquad\;\; = (\; 8 \text{ on denary scale})$$
$$2^2 = 2 \times 2 \qquad\qquad\;\; = (\; 4 \text{ on denary scale})$$
$$2^1 = 2 \qquad\qquad\qquad\; = (\; 2 \text{ on denary scale})$$
$$2^0 = 1 \qquad\qquad\qquad\; = (\; 1 \text{ on denary scale})$$

The binary number 10101 can be easily changed to a number on the denary scale as follows:

2^4	2^3	2^2	2^1	2^0
1	0	1	0	1

$$= (1 \times 2^4) + (0 \times 2^3) + (1 \times 2^2) + (0 \times 2^1) + (1 \times 2^0)$$
$$= \quad 16 \quad + \quad 0 \quad + \quad 4 \quad + \quad 0 \quad + \quad 1$$
$$= 21$$

hence 10101 on the binary scale
$$= 21 \text{ on the denary scale}$$

On the binary scale "tables" are very simple, as follows:

ADDITION TABLE

$$0 + 0 = 0$$
$$0 + 1 = 1$$
$$1 + 0 = 1$$
$$1 + 1 = 10$$

MULTIPLICATION TABLE

$$0 \times 0 = 0$$
$$1 \times 0 = 0$$
$$0 \times 1 = 0$$
$$1 \times 1 = 1$$

Examples of addition, subtraction, multiplication, division are given below alongside the equivalent denary scale working:

1. Addition

```
  1 0 1 1 0 1                    4 5
+     1 1 0 1 1                + 2 7
  ─────────────                ─────
  1 0 0 1 0 0 0                  7 2
```

2. Subtraction

```
  1 1 0 1 1 0 1                1 0 9
−       1 1 1 1 1            −   3 1
  ─────────────              ───────
  1 0 0 1 1 1 0                  7 8
```

N.B. In subtraction when we have 0 minus 1 we have to "borrow" 1 from the column to the left. When taken to the column on the right it is 2, as we are working in powers of 2.

```
e.g.                 1 0 1
                 −     1 1
                 ─────────
                   A B C
```

To find C: 1 minus 1 = 0

To find B: 0 minus 1, "impossible, borrow one from the top line of the column to the left which is 2 when carried to the right".

hence   2 minus 1 = 1

therefore $B = 1$

To find A: 0 minus 0 = 0

therefore $A = 0$

therefore

	Binary	Denary
	1 0 1	5
−	1 1	− 3
	1 0	2

Multiplication

In the binary scale the only processes used are, (a) a shift to the left, (b) addition.

```
        1 0 1 0 1 0 1                  8 5
   ×      1 0 1 0 0 1          ×       4 1
   ─────────────────────          ─────────
        1 0 1 0 1 0 1                  8 5
      1 0 1 0 1 0 1 0 0 0           3 4 0 0
  1 0 1 0 1 0 1 0 0 0 0 0          ─────────
   ─────────────────────           3 4 8 5
  1 1 0 1 1 0 0 1 1 1 0 1
```

Division

Here the only processes used are, (a) a shift to the right, (b) subtraction.

```
              1 0 1 0 · 0 1           6) 6 1 · 5
   110) 1 1 1 1 0 1 · 1              1 0 · 2 5
         1 1 0
         ─────
           1 1 0
           1 1 0
           ─────
             1 1 0
             1 1 0
             ─────
```

N.B. Fractions can be represented by symbols to the right of the bicimal point as on the denary scale.

$$2^{-1} = \frac{1}{2^1} = \frac{1}{2}$$

$$2^{-2} = \frac{1}{2^2} = \frac{1}{4}$$

$$2^{-3} = \frac{1}{2^3} = \frac{1}{8}$$

$$2^{-4} = \frac{1}{2^4} = \frac{1}{16}$$

etc.

hence

·	2^{-1}	2^{-2}	2^{-3}
·	1	0	1

$$1 \times 2^{-1} = 1 \times \tfrac{1}{2} = \tfrac{1}{2}$$

$$0 \times 2^{-2} = 0$$

$$1 \times 2^{-3} = 1 \times \tfrac{1}{8} = \tfrac{1}{8}$$

therefore   0·101 on the binary $= \tfrac{1}{2} + \tfrac{1}{8} = \tfrac{5}{8}$ (denary)

18. CONVERTING A DENARY SCALE NUMBER TO A BINARY SCALE NUMBER

Divide the denary number by 2 until the number is reduced to zero. The remainder at each division (0 or 1) in order represent the corresponding binary number.

Example

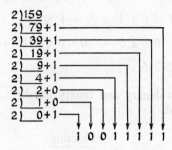

```
2)159
2)  79+1
2)  39+1
2)  19+1
2)   9+1
2)   4+1
2)   2+0
2)   1+0
2)   0+1
     1 0 0 1 1 1 1 1
```

Hence

159 on denary scale = 1 0 0 1 1 1 1 1 on the binary

For fractions, multiply the decimal part only by 2, the whole number part builds up the binary number.

Example

```
      0 · 4 2 5
      _____
× 2   0 · 8 5 0
× 2   1 · 7 0
× 2   1 · 4
× 2   0 · 8        the corresponding binary number is the
× 2   1 · 6        column on the left, i.e.
× 2   1 · 2            0 · 0 1 1 0 1 1 0 0 1 ... etc.
× 2   0 · 4
× 2   0 · 8
× 2   1 · 6
      etc.
```

19. CONVERTING BINARY TO DENARY

Add the powers of 2 as represented by the binary number.

Example

2^7	2^6	2^5	2^4	2^3	2^2	2^1	2^0
1	1	0	1	1	0	0	1

$$= (1 \times 2^7) + (1 \times 2^6) + (1 \times 2^4) + (1 \times 2^3) + (1 \times 2^0)$$
$$= (1 \times 128) + (1 \times 64) + (1 \times 16) + (1 \times 8) + (1 \times 1)$$
$$= \quad 128 \quad + \quad 64 \quad + \quad 16 \quad + \quad 8 \quad + \quad 1$$
$$= 2 \; 1 \; 7$$

For fractions as follows:

Example

.	2^{-1}	2^{-2}	2^{-3}	2^{-4}	2^{-5}
.	1	1	0	1	1

$$= 1 \times \tfrac{1}{2} + 1 \times \tfrac{1}{4} + 1 \times \tfrac{1}{16} + 1 \times \tfrac{1}{32}$$

$$= 0 \cdot 5 + 0 \cdot 2 5 + 0 \cdot 0 6 2 5 + 0 \cdot 0 3 1 2 5$$

$$= 0 \cdot 8 4 3 7 5$$

For working in denary and binary numbers the following conversions are useful.

Decimal	Fraction	Binary
$0 \cdot 5$	$\tfrac{1}{2} = 2^{-1}$	$0 \cdot 1$
$0 \cdot 2 5$	$\tfrac{1}{4} = 2^{-2}$	$0 \cdot 0 1$
$0 \cdot 1 2 5$	$\tfrac{1}{8} = 2^{-3}$	$0 \cdot 0 0 1$
$0 \cdot 0 6 2 5$	$\tfrac{1}{16} = 2^{-4}$	$0 \cdot 0 0 0 1$
$0 \cdot 0 3 1 2 5$	$\tfrac{1}{32} = 2^{-5}$	$0 \cdot 0 0 0 0 1$
$0 \cdot 0 1 5 6 2 5$	$\tfrac{1}{64} = 2^{-6}$	$0 \cdot 0 0 0 0 0 1$

20. OTHER SCALES

Numbers can be written in any scale, and the working is similar to that explained in the binary scale.

Example

Change 325 on the denary scale to base 12.

[Let ten be X and eleven be Y on scale 12.]

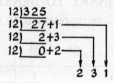

hence

$$325_{10} = 231_{12}$$

This method works for all bases.

Example

Convert $8XY_{12}$ to base 6.

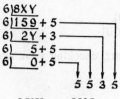

$$\begin{array}{r} 6)\underline{8XY} \\ 6)\underline{159}+5 \\ 6)\underline{\ 2Y}+3 \\ 6)\underline{\ \ 5}+5 \\ 6)\underline{\ \ 0}+5 \end{array}$$

$$5\ 5\ 3\ 5$$

hence $\qquad\qquad 8XY_{12} = 5535_6$

EXERCISE No. 9

1. Construct Addition and Multiplication tables to the following bases:

(a) 3   (b) 4   (c) 6

2. Write down the first 20 numbers in the following scales:

(a) 5   (b) 7   (c) 8

3. Write down the numbers from 15 to 25 (denary scale) in the following scales:

(a) 3   (b) 4   (c) 9

4. Convert each of the following binary numbers into denary numbers:

(i) 1101   (ii) 1110001   (iii) 100001   (iv) 110001
(v) 11110001   (vi) 110010

5. In each part add the binary numbers and check your working by converting to the denary scale:

(i) $1101 + 111 + 101 + 1$
(ii) $1110001 + 100001 + 1101 + 11$
(iii) $11110001 + 110001 + 11001 + 101$

[**Hint:** In checking compare some of the binary numbers with those in Question 1.]

6. Convert the following denary numbers into binary numbers:

(i) 58   (ii) 116   (iii) 260   (iv) 0·625   (v) 7·5   (vi) 16·25

7. In each part subtract, checking your working by converting to the denary scale:

(i) $111101 - 1011$
(ii) $11100001 - 110101$
(iii) $100001 - 1111$

8. Multiply in each part, checking your working by converting to the denary scale:

   (i) 1111 × 101
   (ii) 1011011 × 11001
   (iii) 11000011 × 100101

9. Divide in each part, checking your working by converting to the denary scale:

   (i) 11100 ÷ 100
   (ii) 1001101 ÷ 111
   (iii) 110001100 ÷ 10010

10. Convert each of the following denary numbers into a number on the scale indicated:

(a) 33 (three)	(b) 47 (four)
(c) 107 (five)	(d) 29 (six)
(e) 175 (seven)	(f) 38 (eight)
(g) 212 (nine)	(h) 148 (eleven)
(i) 217 (twelve)	

11. Convert each of the following to the scale of 10:

(a) 123, Scale 7	(b) 3X5, Scale 11
(c) 2Y2, Scale 12	(d) 202, Scale 6
(e) 158, Scale 9	(f) 340, Scale 8
(g) 1010, Scale 5	(h) 1020, Scale 12

12. What advantages might a scale of 12 have over a scale of 10?

13. Show that $1 \, 0_{\text{scale } P} = P_{\text{scale } 10}$
where P is any number on the scale of 10

14. Change each of the following to the base indicated:

(a) 111 on base 3 to base 7	(b) 213 on base 4 to base 5
(c) 100 on base 12 to base 9	(d) 1X7 on base 11 to base 12
(e) 1101101 on base 2 to base 5	(f) 343434 on base 5 to base 9
(g) 7777 on base 11 to base 10	(h) 122120 on base 3 to base 7

15. Add, in the scales indicated:

(a) 12201 (Scale 3)
   1102
	(b) 31021 (Scale 4)
	   3213

(c) 5143 (Scale 6)
   414
	(d) 77067 (Scale 8)
	   3316

(e) 1X943 (Scale 11)
   X19
	(f) 5X3Y (Scale 12)
	   1Y8

16. Treat the 6 parts of Question 15 as subtractions.

17. Treat the 6 parts of Question 15 as multiplications.

18. Treat the 6 parts of Question 15 as divisions, i.e.:

(a) $12201 \div 1102$, etc.

[Give your answers correct to 2 places of "decimals".]

19. In what scales are the following true?

(a) $3 \times 3 = 10$ (b) $4 \times 4 = 31$
(c) $5 \times 5 = 23$ (d) $7 \times 7 = 41$
(e) $3 \times 5 = 17$ (f) $4 \times 6 = 33$

20. What are the even numbers on

(a) Scale 2   (b) Scale 3?

21. What are the odd numbers on

(a) Scale 2   (b) Scale 3?

22. Could 45 represent an even number in some scale?

23. Could 54 represent an odd number in some scale?

24. Find: (a) $55_7 \div 2$ (b) $55_7 \times 2$

25. To ensure that a number is understood to be in decimal notation we write, for example, 24_{10}. Similarly, 12_5 is to be read as meaning that the number is in the scale of 5.

If $p = 12_5$, $q = 24_5$ and $r = 24_{10}$, which of the following statements are true and which false?

(a) $q < r$ (b) $q = 2p$ (c) $p + q = 42_5$ (d) $5q = 240_5$

[O. and C. "O" level, 1964]

Chapter 4

SIMPLE LOGIC

1. Thinking falls roughly into two categories, CREATIVE and ROUTINE. Men such as Shakespeare, Bach, Isaac Newton, Einstein had the ability of creative thought to a marked degree and produced in their own fields work that went beyond established rules. Routine thinking does follow fixed rules, and all of us make use of this way of thinking every day when, for instance, the petrol indicator in the car registers empty, and we deduce that more petrol must be bought.

Computers can be designed to carry out routine thinking operations, but never can they be trained to produce original work.

The study of the rules of thought is called LOGIC and, as thoughts are expressed in words, let us first consider some parts of the language that we use.

2. NOUNS

(a) Proper noun

An individual name is called a proper noun and is usually written with an initial capital letter, for example,

London, Thames, The Alps, Tweedledum

(b) Common noun

Words which refer to a set of objects or things are called common nouns. For example,

car, table, gramophone, chair, mountain, house, gas, plate, tree, river.

Each represents a set in which the members have a common property, e.g.

(i) Deck chair is a subset of chairs

or
$$\{\text{deck chair}\} \subset \{\text{chairs}\}$$
and
$$\{\text{chair}\} \subset \{\text{things upon which one can sit}\}$$

(ii) Some objects can belong to more than one set, and some sets overlap, e.g.

The set of cars and the set of vehicles have members in common

$$\{2 \text{ door cars}\} \subset \{\text{cars}\}$$
$$\{2 \text{ door cars}\} \subset \{\text{vehicles}\}$$

and

$$\{\text{buses}\} \subset \{\text{vehicles}\}$$
but $\{\text{buses}\}$ is **not** $\subset \{\text{cars}\}$

(iii) The set of metals (A) and the set of mammals (B) have no members in common.

$$A \cap B = \phi$$

3. Meaningless sentences, although sometimes amusing, do not convey sense. In the study of logic, therefore, only sentences that have a meaning will be considered.

(*a*) A statement that has a meaning is called a proposition.

(*b*) Simple statements

For example:

It is raining; the meat is cooked; it is hot; television programmes do not stimulate; the house has a blue front door.

The fundamental property of any statement is that it is either

TRUE or FALSE

A statement cannot be both true and false. For example,

"Stupid men are intelligent"

is a false statement!

(*c*) Compound Statements

Easy examples are

(i) It is raining and I must wear a raincoat
(ii) The sea is warm and I want to swim
(iii) Either you stop talking or you will be punished
(iv) I go shopping when the family needs food

When considering compound statements, the validity of the components must be studied, i.e. Are the propositions true or false?

4. SYMBOLS

For many propositions there are many intermediate shades between the black and white of falsehood and truth. However, we will confine ourselves to propositions that are either TRUE or FALSE. This is sometimes called a two-valued system of Logic.

(a) If a statement is made containing a condition such as

"If the lake freezes then I will go ice-skating,"

this can be symbolised as follows:

Let p represent "the lake freezes"

and q represent "I will go ice-skating"

If p then q

or $p \rightarrow q$

which is read, p IMPLIES q.

If both p and q are true, then

$$p \rightarrow q$$

is certainly true, but if p is true and q is false, then

$$p \rightarrow q$$

is definitely false.

The assumption is now made that whenever p is false, $p \rightarrow q$ is **true**.

It is assumed that $p \rightarrow q$ is **false** only if p is true and q is **false**.

These results can be summarised in the following table called a TRUTH TABLE:

	p	q	$p \rightarrow q$
p: "the lake freezes"	T	T	T
q: "I will go ice-skating"	T	F	F
	F	T	T
	F	F	T

If, however, only one of the propositions is true, i.e. p **or** q but not both, then the truth table will be as follows:

p	q	p or q but not both
T	T	F
T	F	T
F	T	T
F	F	F

(b) Statements of the kind

"John will go to France if and, only if, his father will pay," can be symbolised as follows:

Let p represent "John will go to France"

and q represent "his father will pay"

$$p \text{ if, and only if, } q$$

or
$$p \longleftrightarrow q$$

The only possibilities here are

p true, then q true
p false, then q false

and the truth table is as follows:

		p	q	$p \longleftrightarrow q$
p: "John will go to France"		T	T	T
		T	F	F
q: "his father will pay"		F	T	F
		F	F	T

(c) The symbol $\sim$ is read NOT.

For example,

$$\sim p \text{ is read "not } p\text{"}$$

and if p represents "I am cold"

then

$\sim p$ represents "I am not cold".

The table for p and $\sim$ is as follows:

p	$\sim p$
T	F
F	T

(*d*) AND

The symbol used for "AND" is ∧, for example,

$$p \wedge q$$

represents   "It is raining and it is cold."

(*e*) OR

The symbol used for "OR" is ∨, for example,

$$p \vee q$$

represents   "It is raining or it is cold."

Example

"It is raining and it is not cold" is represented by

$$p \wedge \sim q$$

EXERCISE No. 10

1. State whether the following are common or proper nouns:

(*a*) Jane	(*b*) Grass	(*c*) Carpet
(*d*) Devizes	(*e*) Snake	(*f*) Book
(*g*) Air	(*h*) Wood	(*i*) Spectrum

2. State whether the following are true or false:

(*a*) {paper} ⊂ {flax}   (*b*) {water} ⊂ {liquids}
(*c*) {boys} ⊂ {people}   (*d*) {politicians} ⊂ {men}
(*e*) {chickens} ⊂ {birds}   (*f*) {cups} ⊂ {crockery}
(*g*) {chocolate} ⊂ {food}   (*h*) {flutes} ⊂ {wind instruments}

3. What are the simple statements in each of the following compound statements?

(*a*) It is cold and I am warm
(*b*) The sea is inviting, but I do not want to bathe
(*c*) The car was either an estate car or a van
(*d*) Richard and George both like guns
(*e*) Neither you nor I like him

4. Rewrite the following in symbolic form, using the symbols $p, q, \rightarrow, \leftrightarrow, \sim, \wedge, \vee$:

(*a*) If the sum is shining, then it is hot
(*b*) If he gets cross then his mouth will quiver
(*c*) He will marry her only if her father agrees
(*d*) It is not true that he cries if and only if he is hurt
(*e*) The culprit is Smith or Black
(*f*) It is hot and I want to swim
(*g*) It is cold but it is not very dry

5. Construct truth tables for the following:

(a) $(p \lor q) \longleftrightarrow (q \lor p)$
(b) $p \land \sim p$
(c) $(p \to p) \lor (p \to \sim p)$

6. Rewrite the following in symbolic form:

Let p: The sun is shining

Let q: It is warm

(a) If the sun is shining then it is warm
(b) If it is warm then the sun is shining
(c) It is warm if and only if the sun is shining
(d) If it is warm then the sun is not shining
(e) It is not true that it is warm if, and only if, the sun is not shining

7. Construct truth tables for the statements in Question 6.

5. One can think logically without knowing anything of modern mathematics, but logic can be illustrated very clearly by using venn diagrams.

Examples of the use of venn diagrams

(i) Consider the statement

"All metals conduct electricity"

Let $A = \{$all electrical conductors$\}$

$B = \{$metals$\}$

then this statement can be illustrated as follows:

or $B \subset A$ (B is a subset of A)

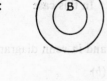

N.B. $A \cup B = A$; $A \cap B = B$

(ii)   "Some boys play cricket"

Let $B = \{$all boys$\}$
$C = \{$all cricketers$\}$

then this, in venn diagram form, can be illustrated as follows:

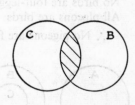

$B \cap C = \{$boys who play cricket$\}$

(iii)

"Some boys do not like soccer"

Let $B = \{$all boys$\}$
$S = \{$people who like soccer$\}$

E

then this can be illustrated as follows:

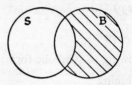

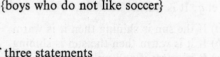

$$S' \cap B = \{\text{boys who do not like soccer}\}$$

6. SYLLOGISMS

These are made up of three statements

1. Major Premise ⎫
2. Minor Premise ⎬ the order of these two does not matter
3. Conclusion   ⎭

(a)

Example

1. All metals conduct electricity
2. Iron is a metal
3. Therefore iron conducts electricity

N.B. The order of statements 1 and 2 could be reversed without altering the conclusion

Let $A = \{\text{electrical conductors}\}$
$\quad B = \{\text{metals}\}$
$\quad C = \{\text{iron}\}$

In this case

$$B \subset A \text{ and } C \subset B$$

and in venn diagram form we have

(b)

Example

No birds are four-legged
All pigeons are birds
∴ No pigeons are four-legged

Let $A = \{\text{four-legged creatures}\}$
$\quad B = \{\text{birds}\}$
$\quad C = \{\text{pigeons}\}$
then $\quad A \cap B = \phi$
$\quad\quad\quad C \subset B$
$\quad\quad\quad C \cap A = \phi$

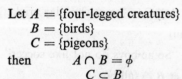

Example

(c) Valid reasoning may lead to a false conclusion if either or both of the premises of a syllogism are false.

For example,

1. All men are honest
2. Soldiers are men
3. All soldiers are honest

Let A = {honest people}
  B = {men}
  C = {soldiers}

The three statements suggest that the venn diagram is as follows:

but, as the statement "All men are honest" is false, the venn diagram is in fact:

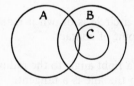

EXERCISE No. 11

1. Use venn diagrams to see whether the following syllogisms are valid:

(a) Some tall men are bald
  Some Englishmen are tall
  Therefore Englishmen are bald

(b) Some Italians do not drink wine
  All Italians are Europeans
  Therefore some Europeans drink wine

(c) No bridge players are stupid
  Some stupid people play pontoon
  Therefore some pontoon players are not bridge players

(d) All soldiers believe in war
  Some of those who believe in war are socialists
  Therefore some socialists are soldiers

(*e*) All comedians make jokes
This man is not a comedian
Therefore he does not make jokes

(*f*) All triangles have 3 angles
This figure is not a triangle
Therefore it does not have 3 angles

(*g*) A polygon is a many-sided figure
This figure is not a quadrilateral
Therefore it is not a polygon

(*h*) No young children smoke
This person does not smoke
Therefore this person is a child

7. CONVERSE

In Geometry care must be taken in stating the converse of a theorem.

Examples

(1) If a line joins the mid-points of two sides of a triangle, then it is parallel and equal in length to one-half of the third side.
CONVERSE
If a line joining two sides of a triangle is parallel and equal in length to one-half of the third side, then it bisects the sides containing it.

(2) If a tangent to a circle is drawn it makes a right-angle to the radius at the point of contact.
CONVERSE
If a line makes a right angle to the radius on the circumference of a circle, then the line is a tangent.

The converse is obtained by reversing the proposition and conclusion: i.e. the converse of "If p, then q" is "If q, then p".

Example

If X has too much to drink X drives fast.

If X drives fast X has had too much to drink.

The second statement is the converse of the first, but it is certainly not true.

N.B. A true proposition need not have a true converse, and vice versa. A false converse is still a converse.

Example

If two lines are each 6 inches long, then they are equal.

The converse is: "If two lines are equal then they are each 6 inches long." It is not true!

From these simple examples it can be seen that it is not valid reasoning to state either the proposition and deduce that the converse is correct or to state the converse and deduce that the proposition is correct.

Many advertisers use this technique to persuade the public to buy their products:

Example

An advertiser shows a beautiful lady using a particular face powder.

The object is to persuade the lady watching that the converse is true, viz. that the face powder makes one beautiful.

Invalid reasoning can also follow from deducing that the opposite of a true proposition is also true.

Example

If two triangles are congruent, then they are equal in area.

In this case the opposite is as follows:

If two triangles are not congruent, then they are not equal in area.

This is not true, as two triangles could be equal in area but not congruent.

Advertisers sometimes state a proposition, hoping that the opposite will be taken as true, or vice versa.

Example

If X's detergent is not used your white shirts will not be really white.

The object here is to suggest that the proposition is correct, viz. that if X's detergent is used, then your white shirts will really be white.

8. STATEMENTS THAT ARE LOGICALLY EQUIVALENT

1. If statement A implies B

   and if statement B implies A

   then A and B are logically equivalent.

Example

(a) If two sides of a triangle are equal, then the angles opposite to these sides are equal.

(b) If two angles are equal, then the sides opposite these angles are equal.

This can be written as follows:

$$\text{If } a \text{ then } b, \quad a \rightarrow b$$

Conversely

$$\text{If } b \text{ then } a, \quad b \rightarrow a$$

$$a \text{ and } b \text{ are equivalent}, \quad a \leftrightarrow b$$

2. A negative of a statement has a similar structure:

Example

(a) If the angles of a polygon do not add up to 180°, then it is not a triangle.

(b) If it is not a triangle, then the angles of a closed polygon do not add up to 180°.

This can be written as follows:

$$\text{If not } a \text{ then not } b, \sim a \to \sim b$$
$$\text{If not } b \text{ then not } a, \sim b \to \sim a$$

3. There is often a temptation to deduce one of the statements from the other and advertisers often use this technique.

Example

"The best is more expensive. X's cigarettes cost 6d. per twenty more than other cigarettes."

It is not logically equivalent that cigarettes that cost 6d. per packet of 20 more than others will be the best.

EXERCISE No. 12

1. Give the converse of each of the following sentences:

(i) If the three angles of a triangle are equal, then the sides are all equal
(ii) If Richard is Barbara's son, then Barbara is Richard's mother
(iii) If the diagonals of a parallelogram intersect at right angles, then it is a rhombus
(iv) If the base angles of a triangle are equal, then the sides opposite these angles are also equal
(v) If the wind is from the south-west, then it will rain
(vi) If you buy "X" cigarettes you are never lonely

2. Give the opposite of each of the sentences in Question 1.

3. Is the conclusion in the following true? If not, say why. The advertiser states that all cars that use "X" petrol get more miles to the gallon. If my car uses "X" petrol I will get more miles to the gallon.

4. An advertiser states that a glamorous lady has soft hands and uses X's soap. What deduction is the advertiser hoping that the consumer will make?

5. An advertiser shows a man working and eating Y's chocolate with a beautiful girl admiring him. What deduction is the advertiser hoping that the consumer will make?

6. Collect examples of advertisements and consider the validity of the claims made by the advertiser.

Chapter 5

MATRICES

1. Before dealing with the algebra of matrices let us first consider a simple coding procedure which Dr G. Matthews has used so successfully and written about in his excellent book.*

2. Suppose an agent wishes to send to his headquarters the following message:

"SEND MONEY NOW"

He decides to replace the letters by numbers using the following code:

A	B	C	D	E	F	G	H	I	J	K	L	M
1	2	3	4	5	6	7	8	9	10	11	12	13

N	O	P	Q	R	S	T	U	V	W	X	Y	Z
14	15	16	17	18	19	20	21	22	23	24	25	26

The message is translated as follows:

SEND   MONEY   NOW
19, 5, 14, 4   13, 15, 14, 5, 25   14, 15, 23

3. If these numbers were sent as they stand it would be very easy to decode the message, so the agent decides to camouflage them by using a set of numbers as an ENCODER and writing the message in a special way, as follows:

Let the encoder be $\begin{pmatrix} 3 & 2 \\ 1 & 1 \end{pmatrix}$

and write the numbers of the message in groups of 4 as follows:

$$\begin{pmatrix} 19 & 5 \\ 14 & 4 \end{pmatrix}; \quad \begin{pmatrix} 13 & 15 \\ 14 & 5 \end{pmatrix}; \quad \begin{pmatrix} 25 & 14 \\ 15 & 23 \end{pmatrix}$$

He uses the encoder by "multiplying" the 3 groups of numbers as follows:

$$\begin{pmatrix} 3 & 2 \\ 1 & 1 \end{pmatrix} \begin{pmatrix} 3 \times 19 + 2 \times 14, \ 3 \times 5 + 2 \times 4 \\ 1 \times 19 + 1 \times 14, \ 1 \times 5 + 1 \times 4 \end{pmatrix} = \begin{pmatrix} 85 & 23 \\ 33 & 9 \end{pmatrix}$$

$$\begin{pmatrix} 19 & 5 \\ 14 & 4 \end{pmatrix}$$

---

* *Contemporary School Mathematics*. First Series. *Matrices I*. G. Matthews. (Arnold).

It will be seen that the numbers in the first row of the encoder,

$$\begin{pmatrix} 3 & 2 \\ 1 & 1 \end{pmatrix}$$

viz.   3 and 2

have been multiplied by the numbers in the first column of

$$\begin{pmatrix} 19 & 5 \\ 14 & 4 \end{pmatrix}$$

viz.   19 and 14

and the results added together i.e.

First row number, 3, × first column number, 19 = 57
Second row number, 2, × second column number, 14 = 28

$$\text{Their sum} = 57 + 28 = 85$$

and similarly for the other numbers.

N.B. Multiply with the encoder in front of the group being multiplied.

The second group $\begin{pmatrix} 13 & 15 \\ 14 & 5 \end{pmatrix}$ becomes

$$\begin{pmatrix} 3 & 2 \\ 1 & 1 \end{pmatrix} \begin{pmatrix} 3 \times 13 + 2 \times 14, & 3 \times 15 + 2 \times 5 \\ 1 \times 13 + 1 \times 14, & 1 \times 15 + 1 \times 5 \end{pmatrix} = \begin{pmatrix} 67 & 55 \\ 27 & 20 \end{pmatrix}$$

$$\begin{pmatrix} 13 & 15 \\ 14 & 5 \end{pmatrix}$$

The third group $\begin{pmatrix} 25 & 14 \\ 15 & 23 \end{pmatrix}$ becomes

$$\begin{pmatrix} 3 & 2 \\ 1 & 1 \end{pmatrix} \begin{pmatrix} 3 \times 25 + 2 \times 15, & 3 \times 14 + 2 \times 23 \\ 1 \times 25 + 1 \times 15, & 1 \times 14 + 1 \times 23 \end{pmatrix} = \begin{pmatrix} 105 & 88 \\ 40 & 37 \end{pmatrix}$$

$$\begin{pmatrix} 25 & 14 \\ 15 & 23 \end{pmatrix}$$

The original numbers have been changed to

$$\begin{pmatrix} 85 & 23 \\ 33 & 9 \end{pmatrix}; \quad \begin{pmatrix} 67 & 55 \\ 27 & 20 \end{pmatrix}; \quad \begin{pmatrix} 105 & 88 \\ 40 & 37 \end{pmatrix}$$

and the message is sent by the agent as follows:

85, 23, 33, 9, 67, 55, 27, 20, 105, 88, 40, 37

4. Headquarters, on receiving this message, proceeds to decode it by using a DECODER $\begin{pmatrix} 1 & -2 \\ -1 & 3 \end{pmatrix}$

and rewriting the message into groups of 4 numbers as follows:

$$\begin{pmatrix} 85 & 23 \\ 33 & 9 \end{pmatrix}; \quad \begin{pmatrix} 67 & 55 \\ 27 & 20 \end{pmatrix}; \quad \begin{pmatrix} 105 & 88 \\ 40 & 37 \end{pmatrix}$$

These are decoded in a similar way to the coding process, except that now the decoder $\begin{pmatrix} 1 & -2 \\ -1 & 3 \end{pmatrix}$ is used and placed first when multiplying

(i)

$$\begin{pmatrix} 1 & -2 \\ -1 & 3 \end{pmatrix} \begin{pmatrix} 1 \times 85 - 2 \times 33, & 1 \times 23 - 2 \times 9 \\ -1 \times 85 + 3 \times 33, & -1 \times 23 + 3 \times 9 \end{pmatrix} = \begin{pmatrix} 19 & 5 \\ 14 & 4 \end{pmatrix}$$

$$\begin{pmatrix} 85 & 23 \\ 33 & 9 \end{pmatrix}$$

(ii)

$$\begin{pmatrix} 1 & -2 \\ -1 & 3 \end{pmatrix} \begin{pmatrix} 1 \times 67 - 2 \times 27, & 1 \times 55 - 2 \times 20 \\ -1 \times 67 + 3 \times 27, & -1 \times 55 + 3 \times 20 \end{pmatrix} = \begin{pmatrix} 13 & 15 \\ 14 & 5 \end{pmatrix}$$

$$\begin{pmatrix} 67 & 55 \\ 27 & 20 \end{pmatrix}$$

(iii)

$$\begin{pmatrix} 1 & -2 \\ -1 & 3 \end{pmatrix} \begin{pmatrix} 1 \times 105 - 2 \times 40, & 1 \times 88 - 2 \times 37 \\ -1 \times 105 + 3 \times 40, & -1 \times 88 + 3 \times 37 \end{pmatrix} = \begin{pmatrix} 25 & 14 \\ 15 & 23 \end{pmatrix}$$

$$\begin{pmatrix} 105 & 88 \\ 40 & 37 \end{pmatrix}$$

The decoded numbers are written as follows:

$$19, 5, 14, 4, 13, 15, 14, 5, 25, 14, 15, 23$$

and using $A = 1$, $B = 2$, $C = 3$, etc., the message is read

"SEND MONEY NOW"

5. If the message could not exactly be divided into groups of 4, then letters such as Z could have been added or zeros, e.g.

$$\begin{array}{cccccccc} M & A & T & H & S & . & . & . \\ 13, & 1, & 20, & 8, & 19, & 0, & 0, & 0 \end{array}$$

thus making 2 groups of 4.

Using the same encoder as before

$$\begin{pmatrix} 3 & 2 \\ 1 & 1 \end{pmatrix}$$

The message becomes

(i) $\begin{pmatrix} 3 & 2 \\ 1 & 1 \end{pmatrix} \begin{pmatrix} 3 \times 13 + 2 \times 20, & 3 \times 1 + 2 \times 8 \\ 1 \times 13 + 1 \times 20, & 1 \times 1 + 1 \times 8 \end{pmatrix} = \begin{pmatrix} 79 & 19 \\ 33 & 9 \end{pmatrix}$

$$\begin{pmatrix} 13 & 1 \\ 20 & 8 \end{pmatrix}$$

(ii) $\begin{pmatrix} 3 & 2 \\ 1 & 1 \end{pmatrix} \begin{pmatrix} 3 \times 19 + 2 \times 0, & 3 \times 0 + 2 \times 0 \\ 1 \times 19 + 1 \times 0, & 1 \times 0 + 1 \times 0 \end{pmatrix} = \begin{pmatrix} 57 & 0 \\ 19 & 0 \end{pmatrix}$

$$\begin{pmatrix} 19 & 0 \\ 0 & 0 \end{pmatrix}$$

and is sent thus: 79, 19, 33, 9, 57, 0, 19, 0

6. The decoding is done as before, using as the decoder

$$\begin{pmatrix} 1 & -2 \\ -1 & 3 \end{pmatrix}$$

(i)

$$\begin{pmatrix} 1 & -2 \\ -1 & 3 \end{pmatrix} \begin{pmatrix} 1 \times 79 - 2 \times 33, & 1 \times 19 - 2 \times 9 \\ -1 \times 79 + 3 \times 33, & -1 \times 19 + 3 \times 9 \end{pmatrix} = \begin{pmatrix} 13 & 1 \\ 20 & 8 \end{pmatrix}$$

$$\begin{pmatrix} 79 & 19 \\ 33 & 9 \end{pmatrix}$$

(ii)

$$\begin{pmatrix} 1 & -2 \\ -1 & 3 \end{pmatrix} \begin{pmatrix} 1 \times 57 - 2 \times 19, & 1 \times 0 - 2 \times 0 \\ -1 \times 57 + 3 \times 19, & -1 \times 0 + 3 \times 0 \end{pmatrix} = \begin{pmatrix} 19 & 0 \\ 0 & 0 \end{pmatrix}$$

$$\begin{pmatrix} 57 & 0 \\ 19 & 0 \end{pmatrix}$$

The numbers 13, 1, 20, 8, 19, 0, 0, 0, are then read as MATHS.

EXERCISE No. 13

Use the code A = 1, B = 2, C = 3, etc., the encoder $\begin{pmatrix} 3 & 2 \\ 1 & 1 \end{pmatrix}$ and the decoder $\begin{pmatrix} 1 & -2 \\ -1 & 3 \end{pmatrix}$ in the following examples:

[Multiply with the encoder or decoder in front.]

1. encode

   (a) SOOT   (b) COME   (c) SCHOOL
   (d) ANT   (e) A FINE DAY   (f) ALL MAD
   (g) I LIKE CURRY

2. decode

   (a) 36, 73, 17, 29
   (b) 30, 98, 13, 40, 15, 0, 5, 0
   (c) 89, 21 38, 10, 99, 85, 40, 35
   (d) 49, 75, 21, 30, 69, 0, 23, 0
   (e) 78, 62, 29, 27, 37, 59, 14, 20, 57, 75, 19, 25

3. encode

"FIVE ENEMY PLANES SABOTAGED"

7. The arrangement of numbers when written as, for example,

$$\begin{pmatrix} 13 & 1 \\ 20 & 8 \end{pmatrix}$$

is called a MATRIX.

8. A SQUARE MATRIX has the same number of rows as columns, for example,

$$\begin{pmatrix} 2 & 5 \\ 3 & 1 \end{pmatrix}; \qquad \begin{pmatrix} 2 & 3 & 4 \\ 1 & 0 & 1 \\ 2 & 3 & 1 \end{pmatrix} \text{ etc.}$$

9. The algebra of matrices will be considered before applying them to other problems.

DEFINITION

A matrix is a rectangular array of numbers.

(*a*) Square matrix.

Example

$$\begin{pmatrix} 1 & 2 \\ 3 & 4 \end{pmatrix}$$

in which there are 2 rows and 2 columns. The rows are horizontal and the columns vertical. In this example one row contains the numbers 1 and 2 and the second row contains 3 and 4.

One column is 1 and 3, and the second column is 2 and 4.

(*b*) Rectangular matrix.

Example

$$\begin{pmatrix} 1 & 2 & 3 \\ 4 & 5 & 6 \end{pmatrix}$$

in which there are 2 rows and 3 columns.

Rows: 1, 2, 3, and 4, 5, 6

Columns: 1, 4; 2, 5; and 3, 6

10. ADDITION OF MATRICES

Add the corresponding components separately.

Example

$$\begin{pmatrix} 1 & 2 \\ 3 & 4 \end{pmatrix} + \begin{pmatrix} 5 & 6 \\ 7 & 8 \end{pmatrix} = \begin{pmatrix} 6 & 8 \\ 10 & 12 \end{pmatrix}$$

Example

$$\begin{pmatrix} 2 & -3 \\ -2 & 5 \end{pmatrix} + \begin{pmatrix} 1 & -1 \\ -1 & 3 \end{pmatrix} = \begin{pmatrix} 3 & -4 \\ -3 & 8 \end{pmatrix}$$

$$\begin{pmatrix} 5 & 6 \\ -2 & -3 \end{pmatrix} + \begin{pmatrix} -5 & -6 \\ 2 & 3 \end{pmatrix} = \begin{pmatrix} 0 & 0 \\ 0 & 0 \end{pmatrix}$$

11. MULTIPLICATION OF A MATRIX BY A SCALAR

(*a*) Repeated addition of the same matrix, e.g.

$$\begin{pmatrix} 1 & 2 \\ 3 & 4 \end{pmatrix} + \begin{pmatrix} 1 & 2 \\ 3 & 4 \end{pmatrix} = \begin{pmatrix} 2 & 4 \\ 6 & 8 \end{pmatrix}$$

can be written as follows:

$$2\begin{pmatrix} 1 & 2 \\ 3 & 4 \end{pmatrix} = \begin{pmatrix} 2 & 4 \\ 6 & 8 \end{pmatrix}$$

Each of the components of the matrix is multiplied by the scalar number. Scalars are real numbers.

(*b*) Geometrically, multiplication of a matrix by a scalar can be shown as follows:

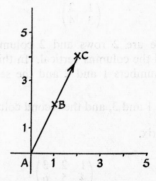

The line *AB* joins the origin (0   0) to the point (1   2).

If we double the length of the line the arrow (line *AB*) will arrive at the point (2   4), point *C*. The scale factor is 2.

(*c*)

Further example

$$3\begin{pmatrix} -2 & 3 \\ 1 & -1 \end{pmatrix} = \begin{pmatrix} -6 & 9 \\ 3 & -3 \end{pmatrix}$$

The scalar in this case is 3.

12. ZERO ELEMENT

Consider the example

$$\begin{pmatrix} 5 & 6 \\ -2 & -3 \end{pmatrix} + \begin{pmatrix} -5 & -6 \\ 2 & 3 \end{pmatrix} = \begin{pmatrix} 0 & 0 \\ 0 & 0 \end{pmatrix}$$

or   *A*   +   *B*   =   0

B is the negative of *A*, and when *A* and *B* are added we get the ZERO MATRIX.

If 0 is added to any matrix we have:

$$\begin{pmatrix} 1 & 2 \\ 3 & 4 \end{pmatrix} + \begin{pmatrix} 0 & 0 \\ 0 & 0 \end{pmatrix} = \begin{pmatrix} 1 & 2 \\ 3 & 4 \end{pmatrix}$$

Adding the zero matrix makes no difference.

13. MULTIPLICATION OF MATRICES

In the example on coding, multiplication of matrices was used, but the algebra of multiplication is repeated here.

First, a simple example:

Example

$$A = \begin{pmatrix} 1 & 2 \\ 3 & 4 \end{pmatrix}; \qquad B = \begin{pmatrix} 5 & 6 \\ 7 & 8 \end{pmatrix}$$

$$A \cdot B = \begin{pmatrix} 1 & 2 \\ 3 & 4 \end{pmatrix} \begin{pmatrix} 5 & 6 \\ 7 & 8 \end{pmatrix}$$

$$= \begin{pmatrix} 1 \times 5 + 2 \times 7 & 1 \times 6 + 2 \times 8 \\ 3 \times 5 + 4 \times 7 & 3 \times 6 + 4 \times 8 \end{pmatrix}$$

$$= \begin{pmatrix} 19 & 22 \\ 43 & 50 \end{pmatrix}$$

In general, if $A = \begin{pmatrix} a & b \\ c & d \end{pmatrix}$ and $B = \begin{pmatrix} e & f \\ g & h \end{pmatrix}$

$$A \cdot B = \begin{pmatrix} a & b \\ c & d \end{pmatrix} \begin{pmatrix} e & f \\ g & h \end{pmatrix} = \begin{pmatrix} ae + bg & af + bh \\ ce + dg & cf + dh \end{pmatrix}$$

14. MULTIPLICATION IS NOT COMMUTATIVE

In arithmetic $2 \times 3 = 3 \times 2$

Let us see what happens in matrix multiplication.

In paragraph 13 we saw that

$$A \cdot B = \begin{pmatrix} 1 & 2 \\ 3 & 4 \end{pmatrix} \begin{pmatrix} 5 & 6 \\ 7 & 8 \end{pmatrix} = \begin{pmatrix} 19 & 22 \\ 43 & 50 \end{pmatrix}$$

What is the product $B.A$?

$$B \cdot A = \begin{pmatrix} 5 & 6 \\ 7 & 8 \end{pmatrix} \begin{pmatrix} 1 & 2 \\ 3 & 4 \end{pmatrix}$$

$$= \begin{pmatrix} 5 \times 1 + 6 \times 3 & 5 \times 2 + 6 \times 4 \\ 7 \times 1 + 8 \times 3 & 7 \times 2 + 8 \times 4 \end{pmatrix} = \begin{pmatrix} 23 & 34 \\ 31 & 46 \end{pmatrix}$$

It is **not** the same as $A.B$, i.e. $A \cdot B$ **does not equal** $B \cdot A$.

Therefore with matrix multiplication one must be very careful about the order in which the elements are multiplied.

15. UNITY ELEMENT

Consider the matrix $\begin{pmatrix} 1 & 0 \\ 0 & 1 \end{pmatrix}$

Multiplying by this we have:

Example

$$\begin{pmatrix} 1 & 2 \\ 3 & 4 \end{pmatrix} \begin{pmatrix} 1 & 0 \\ 0 & 1 \end{pmatrix} = \begin{pmatrix} 1 \times 1 + 2 \times 0 & 1 \times 0 + 2 \times 1 \\ 3 \times 1 + 4 \times 0 & 3 \times 0 + 4 \times 1 \end{pmatrix} = \begin{pmatrix} 1 & 2 \\ 3 & 4 \end{pmatrix}$$

also:

$$\begin{pmatrix} 1 & 0 \\ 0 & 1 \end{pmatrix} \begin{pmatrix} 1 & 2 \\ 3 & 4 \end{pmatrix} = \begin{pmatrix} 1 \times 1 + 3 \times 0 & 1 \times 2 + 0 \times 4 \\ 0 \times 1 + 1 \times 3 & 0 \times 2 + 1 \times 4 \end{pmatrix} = \begin{pmatrix} 1 & 2 \\ 3 & 4 \end{pmatrix}$$

hence $\quad \begin{pmatrix} 1 & 2 \\ 3 & 4 \end{pmatrix} \begin{pmatrix} 1 & 0 \\ 0 & 1 \end{pmatrix} = \begin{pmatrix} 1 & 2 \\ 3 & 4 \end{pmatrix} = \begin{pmatrix} 1 & 0 \\ 0 & 1 \end{pmatrix} \begin{pmatrix} 1 & 2 \\ 3 & 4 \end{pmatrix}$

If we multiply a matrix by $\begin{pmatrix} 1 & 0 \\ 0 & 1 \end{pmatrix}$ from either the left or right the result is the same, viz. the original matrix.

The matrix $\begin{pmatrix} 1 & 0 \\ 0 & 1 \end{pmatrix}$ is called the UNIT MATRIX, and is often denoted by the letter I_2. [$I_1 = (1)$.]

EXERCISE No. 14

Add the following matrices:

1. $\begin{pmatrix} 3 & 2 \\ 1 & 4 \end{pmatrix} + \begin{pmatrix} -1 + 3 \\ 2 + 0 \end{pmatrix}$ 2. $\begin{pmatrix} 5 & -5 \\ 2 & 3 \end{pmatrix} + \begin{pmatrix} -5 & 5 \\ -2 & -3 \end{pmatrix}$

3. $\begin{pmatrix} a & b \\ c & d \end{pmatrix} + \begin{pmatrix} w & x \\ y & z \end{pmatrix}$

Find the following scalar products:

4. $2 \begin{pmatrix} 3 & -2 \\ 0 & 4 \end{pmatrix}$ 5. $-3 \begin{pmatrix} -1 & 3 \\ -3 & 4 \end{pmatrix}$ 6. $p \begin{pmatrix} a & b \\ c & d \end{pmatrix}$

Find the following matrix products:

7. $\begin{pmatrix} 2 & 1 \\ -1 & 3 \end{pmatrix} \begin{pmatrix} 0 & 3 \\ 2 & 1 \end{pmatrix}$ 8. $\begin{pmatrix} 0 & 3 \\ 2 & 1 \end{pmatrix} \begin{pmatrix} 2 & 1 \\ -1 & 3 \end{pmatrix}$

9. $\begin{pmatrix} -1 & 1 \\ 1 & -1 \end{pmatrix} \begin{pmatrix} 2 & 3 \\ 4 & 5 \end{pmatrix}$ 10. $\begin{pmatrix} 2 & 3 \\ 4 & 5 \end{pmatrix} \begin{pmatrix} -1 & 1 \\ 1 & -1 \end{pmatrix}$

11. $\begin{pmatrix} 2 & 3 \\ -3 & 2 \end{pmatrix} \begin{pmatrix} 2 & 0 \\ 0 & 2 \end{pmatrix}$ 12. $\begin{pmatrix} 2 & 0 \\ 0 & 2 \end{pmatrix} \begin{pmatrix} 2 & 3 \\ -3 & 2 \end{pmatrix}$

13. What do you notice about the answers to Questions 11 and 12?

14. $\begin{pmatrix} 1 & 0 \\ 0 & 1 \end{pmatrix} \begin{pmatrix} a & b \\ c & d \end{pmatrix} = ?$

15. $A = \begin{pmatrix} 2 & 1 \\ 4 & 3 \end{pmatrix}$; $B = \begin{pmatrix} 1 & 2 \\ 4 & 5 \end{pmatrix}$

Find:

(a) $A + B$ (b) $B + A$
(c) $A . B$ (d) $B . A$

16. $A = \begin{pmatrix} 0 & 1 \\ 2 & 3 \end{pmatrix}$; $B = \begin{pmatrix} -1 & 2 \\ 4 & 3 \end{pmatrix}$; $C = \begin{pmatrix} 2 & -1 \\ 6 & 5 \end{pmatrix}$

Find:

(a) $B + C$ (b) $A(B + C)$ (c) $A . B$
(d) $A . C$ (e) $A . B + A . C$
(f) Is $A(B + C) = A . B + A . C$?   (g) $(B + C)A$
(h) $B . A$ (i) $C . A$ (j) $B . A + C . A$
(k) Is $B . A + C . A = (B + C)A$?
(l) Is $A(B + C) = (B + C)A$?

16. THE INVERSE OF A MATRIX
Example

(a) $\begin{pmatrix} 3 & 5 \\ 1 & 2 \end{pmatrix} \begin{pmatrix} 2 & -5 \\ -1 & 3 \end{pmatrix} = \begin{pmatrix} 1 & 0 \\ 0 & 1 \end{pmatrix} = I_2$, the unit matrix.   The matrix

$\begin{pmatrix} 2 & -5 \\ -1 & 3 \end{pmatrix}$ is the INVERSE of $\begin{pmatrix} 3 & 5 \\ 1 & 2 \end{pmatrix}$ because when the two matrices
are multiplied together their product $= I_2$

N.B. $\begin{pmatrix} 2 & -5 \\ -1 & 3 \end{pmatrix} \begin{pmatrix} 3 & 5 \\ 1 & 2 \end{pmatrix} = \begin{pmatrix} 1 & 0 \\ 0 & 1 \end{pmatrix}$

(b) The decoder that was used earlier in the chapter will be seen to
be the inverse of the encoder. Hence their product is I_2, the unit
matrix, e.g.

$$\text{encoder} = \begin{pmatrix} 3 & 2 \\ 1 & 1 \end{pmatrix}; \qquad \text{decoder} = \begin{pmatrix} 1 & -2 \\ -1 & 3 \end{pmatrix}$$

$$\begin{pmatrix} 3 & 2 \\ 1 & 1 \end{pmatrix} \begin{pmatrix} 3-2, & -6+6 \\ 1-1, & -2+3 \end{pmatrix} = \begin{pmatrix} 1 & 0 \\ 0 & 1 \end{pmatrix}$$
$$\begin{pmatrix} 1 & -2 \\ -1 & 3 \end{pmatrix}$$

and

$$\begin{pmatrix} 1 & -2 \\ -1 & 3 \end{pmatrix} \begin{pmatrix} 3-2, & 2-2 \\ -3+3, & -2+3 \end{pmatrix} = \begin{pmatrix} 1 & 0 \\ 0 & 1 \end{pmatrix}$$
$$\begin{pmatrix} 3 & 2 \\ 1 & 1 \end{pmatrix}$$

(c) Let $E = \begin{pmatrix} 3 & 2 \\ 1 & 1 \end{pmatrix}$ and $A = \begin{pmatrix} -2 & 1 \\ 0 & 3 \end{pmatrix}$

hence $\qquad\qquad E.A = \begin{pmatrix} -6 & 9 \\ -2 & 4 \end{pmatrix} = B$, say,

$$E^{-1} = \begin{pmatrix} 1 & -2 \\ -1 & 3 \end{pmatrix}$$

$$E^{-1}.B = \begin{pmatrix} -2 & 1 \\ 0 & 3 \end{pmatrix}$$

hence in symbols we have

$$E.A = B$$
$$E^{-1}.E.A = E^{-1}.B$$

but $\qquad\qquad E^{-1}.E = I_2$, the unit matrix

$$A = E^{-1}.B$$

N.B. The inverse of the matrix P is usually written p^{-1}, hence $p^{-1}p = I$.

17. The determinant of a matrix is defined as follows:

Let matrix $= \begin{pmatrix} a & b \\ c & d \end{pmatrix}$

where a, b, c and d are real numbers, then the Determinant of the matrix

$$= ad - bc$$

If the multiplication of matrices is to be reversible, then the determinant must not be zero,

i.e. If in the coding example the encoder had been $\begin{pmatrix} 4 & 2 \\ 2 & 1 \end{pmatrix}$ then its determinant $= 4 \times 1 - 2 \times 2 = 0$ and there is no corresponding decoder so that it would be impossible to decode any message sent using this encoder.

18. What is the inverse of $\begin{pmatrix} a & b \\ c & d \end{pmatrix}$?

Let the inverse $= \begin{pmatrix} p & q \\ r & s \end{pmatrix}$

Then $\qquad\qquad \begin{pmatrix} p & q \\ r & s \end{pmatrix} \begin{pmatrix} a & b \\ c & d \end{pmatrix} = \begin{pmatrix} 1 & 0 \\ 0 & 1 \end{pmatrix}$

Hence by matrix multiplication

(1) $ap + qc = 1$

(2) $pb + qd = 0 \Rightarrow q = \dfrac{-pb}{d}$

(3) $ra + sc = 0 \Rightarrow r = \dfrac{-sc}{a}$

(4) $rb + sd = 1$

Substituting for q in equation (1) we have

$$ap \frac{-pbc}{d} = 1 \Rightarrow apd - pbc = d$$

$$\Rightarrow p = \frac{d}{ad - bc}$$

Hence $$q = \frac{-b}{d}\left(\frac{d}{ad - bc}\right) = \frac{-b}{ad - bc}$$

Substituting for r in equation (4), we find that

$$r = \frac{-c}{ad - bc}$$

and $$s = \frac{a}{ad - bc}$$

Let $$ad - bc = \triangle$$

then the inverse of $$\begin{pmatrix} a & b \\ c & d \end{pmatrix}$$

is $$\begin{pmatrix} \dfrac{d}{\triangle} & \dfrac{-b}{\triangle} \\ \dfrac{-c}{\triangle} & \dfrac{a}{\triangle} \end{pmatrix} \text{ or } \frac{1}{\triangle}\begin{pmatrix} d & -b \\ -c & a \end{pmatrix}$$

Example

Find the inverse of $$\begin{pmatrix} 3 & -4 \\ 4 & -2 \end{pmatrix}$$

Its determinant $$= -6 - (-16) = +10$$

The inverse $$= \begin{pmatrix} -\frac{2}{10} & \frac{4}{10} \\ -\frac{4}{10} & \frac{3}{10} \end{pmatrix}$$

Check

$$\begin{pmatrix} -\frac{2}{10} & \frac{4}{10} \\ -\frac{4}{10} & \frac{3}{10} \end{pmatrix} \begin{pmatrix} -\frac{6}{10} + \frac{16}{10} & +\frac{8}{10} - \frac{8}{10} \\ -\frac{12}{10} + \frac{12}{10} & +\frac{16}{10} - \frac{6}{10} \end{pmatrix} = \begin{pmatrix} 1 & 0 \\ 0 & 1 \end{pmatrix}$$

$$\begin{pmatrix} 3 & -4 \\ 4 & -2 \end{pmatrix}$$

Example

In paragraph 17 it was stated that there is no decoder if the encoder is $\begin{pmatrix} 4 & 2 \\ 2 & 1 \end{pmatrix}$. The Determinant $= 0$

hence the decoder $= \begin{pmatrix} \frac{1}{0} & -\frac{2}{0} \\ -\frac{2}{0} & \frac{4}{0} \end{pmatrix}$

and since $\frac{1}{0}$, $-\frac{2}{0}$, $-\frac{2}{0}$, $\frac{4}{0}$ are not definable then the decoder does not exist.

F

To summarise this statement:
The inverse of a matrix cannot be found when the determinant of a matrix is zero.

EXERCISE No. 15

1. Find the determinants of the following matrices:

(a) $\begin{pmatrix} 5 & 2 \\ 3 & 4 \end{pmatrix}$ (b) $\begin{pmatrix} -2 & -3 \\ 1 & -1 \end{pmatrix}$ (c) $\begin{pmatrix} 0 & 1 \\ 1 & 6 \end{pmatrix}$

(d) $\begin{pmatrix} 5 & 0 \\ 2 & -3 \end{pmatrix}$ (e) $\begin{pmatrix} -a+q \\ -p+b \end{pmatrix}$ (f) $\begin{pmatrix} -1 & 3 \\ 2 & 7 \end{pmatrix}$

(g) $\begin{pmatrix} 0 & 1 \\ -1 & 0 \end{pmatrix}$ (h) $\begin{pmatrix} 6 & 3 \\ 2 & 1 \end{pmatrix}$ (i) $\begin{pmatrix} 3 & 0 \\ 0 & 3 \end{pmatrix}$

2. Find the inverses of the matrices in Question 1.

3. Check your answers to Question 2 by multiplying the inverse by the original matrix and showing that the product is I (the unit matrix), or that the inverse does not exist.

4. Let us call a matrix of the form $\begin{pmatrix} p & 0 \\ 0 & q \end{pmatrix}$

a P-matrix, and one of the form $\begin{pmatrix} 0 & r \\ s & 0 \end{pmatrix}$

a Q-matrix, where no one of p, q, r, s is zero.

Which of the following are true, which false?

(a) The unit matrix is a Q-matrix
(b) The square of a P-matrix is a Q-matrix
(c) The product of a P-matrix and a Q-matrix can never be the zero matrix
(d) The inverse of a Q-matrix is a P-matrix

[O. and C. "O" level, 1964]

19. RECTANGULAR MATRICES

Two matrices can be multiplied provided that there are the same number of columns in the first matrix as rows in the second.

Example

$$A = \begin{pmatrix} 2 & 3 \\ 0 & 1 \\ 1 & 2 \end{pmatrix} \qquad B = \begin{pmatrix} 1 & 2 & 3 \\ 4 & 5 & 6 \end{pmatrix}$$

A has 3 rows and 2 columns and is a 3 by 2 matrix.
B has 2 rows and 3 columns and is a 2 by 3 matrix.

$$AB = \begin{pmatrix} 2 & 3 \\ 0 & 1 \\ 1 & 2 \end{pmatrix} \begin{pmatrix} 1 & 2 & 3 \\ 4 & 5 & 6 \end{pmatrix} = \begin{pmatrix} 14 & 19 & 24 \\ 4 & 5 & 6 \\ 9 & 12 & 15 \end{pmatrix}$$

The product matrix is a 3 by 3 matrix.

If w, x, y and z are real numbers, then

A (w by x) matrix multiplied by

a (y by z) matrix

is **possible** if the **two** middle numbers are the same, $x = y$

i.e. the number of columns in the first matrix

= number of rows in the second matrix

The result is a (w by z) matrix.

i.e. it has the same number of rows as the first matrix and the same number of columns as the second matrix.

Example

A = (5 by 4) matrix multiplied by B = (4 by 1) matrix is **possible** and gives a (5 by 1) matrix.

$$
\begin{matrix}
5 \text{ rows and} \\
4 \text{ columns}
\end{matrix}
\begin{pmatrix}
1 & 2 & 3 & 4 \\
0 & 1 & 0 & 1 \\
2 & 1 & 0 & 1 \\
3 & 0 & 2 & 0 \\
4 & 2 & 0 & 2
\end{pmatrix}
\begin{pmatrix}
1 \\ 2 \\ 3 \\ 4
\end{pmatrix}
\begin{matrix}
4 \text{ rows} \\
\text{and} \\
1 \text{ column}
\end{matrix}
$$

$$
\text{Product} =
\begin{pmatrix}
1 + 4 + 9 + 16 \\
2 + 4 \\
2 + 2 + 4 \\
3 + 6 \\
4 + 4 + 8
\end{pmatrix}
=
\begin{pmatrix}
30 \\ 6 \\ 8 \\ 9 \\ 16
\end{pmatrix}
\begin{matrix}
5 \text{ rows} \\
\text{and} \\
1 \text{ column}
\end{matrix}
$$

Example

$$
\begin{matrix}
2 \text{ rows and} \\
3 \text{ columns}
\end{matrix}
\begin{pmatrix}
1 & 2 & 3 \\
4 & 5 & 6
\end{pmatrix}
\text{ multiplied by }
\begin{pmatrix}
0 & 1 & 2 \\
1 & 0 & 1
\end{pmatrix}
\begin{matrix}
2 \text{ rows} \\
3 \text{ columns}
\end{matrix}
$$

This is **impossible**.

A (2 by 3) matrix cannot be multiplied by a (2 by 3) matrix.

EXERCISE No. 16

1. Find the following matrix products:

(a) $\begin{pmatrix} 2 & 3 \\ 1 & 0 \end{pmatrix} \begin{pmatrix} 1 \\ 2 \end{pmatrix}$

(b) $\begin{pmatrix} 2 & 0 & 1 \\ 0 & 2 & 3 \end{pmatrix} \begin{pmatrix} 3 \\ 0 \\ 1 \end{pmatrix}$

(c) $(2 \ 3 \ 1 \ 4) \begin{pmatrix} 1 & 0 \\ 0 & 2 \\ -1 & 3 \\ 0 & -1 \end{pmatrix}$

(d) $\begin{pmatrix} -1 & 0 & -2 & 3 \\ 0 & 2 & 1 & -2 \end{pmatrix} \begin{pmatrix} -2 \\ +1 \\ 0 \\ +3 \end{pmatrix}$

(e) $\begin{pmatrix} 2 & 1 \\ -1 & 0 \end{pmatrix} (3 \ 4)$

(f) $(3 \ 4) \begin{pmatrix} 2 & 1 \\ -1 & 0 \end{pmatrix}$

2. Find the following matrix products:

(a) $\begin{pmatrix} 2 & 3 & 1 \\ 1 & 0 & -1 \end{pmatrix} \begin{pmatrix} 1 & 2 \\ 3 & -1 \\ 4 & 5 \end{pmatrix}$ (b) $\begin{pmatrix} 1 & 3 & 1 & 2 \\ -1 & 0 & -1 & 2 \end{pmatrix} \begin{pmatrix} a \\ -a \\ 2a \\ 3a \end{pmatrix}$

(c) $\begin{pmatrix} 1 & 3 & 0 \\ 7 & -1 & 3 \\ -2 & 0 & 0 \end{pmatrix} \begin{pmatrix} 3 \\ -1 \\ 1 \end{pmatrix}$ (d) $\begin{pmatrix} 3 \\ -1 \\ 1 \end{pmatrix} \begin{pmatrix} 1 & 3 & 0 \\ 7 & -1 & 3 \\ -2 & 0 & 0 \end{pmatrix}$

(e) $\begin{pmatrix} 0 & 0 & 1 & -1 \\ -1 & 1 & 0 & 0 \\ 1 & 0 & 0 & 2 \end{pmatrix} \begin{pmatrix} 1 & -1 & 0 \\ 0 & 1 & -2 \\ -1 & 0 & 0 \\ 2 & 1 & -1 \end{pmatrix}$

20. SOLUTION OF 2 LINEAR EQUATIONS IN 2 UNKNOWNS

Solve for x and y, using matrices:

$$\begin{cases} 5x + 2y = 9 \\ 7x + 3y = 13 \end{cases}$$

$$\begin{pmatrix} 5 & 2 \\ 7 & 3 \end{pmatrix} \begin{pmatrix} x \\ y \end{pmatrix} = \begin{pmatrix} 5x + 2y \\ 7x + 3y \end{pmatrix}$$

Rewriting:

$$\begin{pmatrix} 5 & 2 \\ 7 & 3 \end{pmatrix} \begin{pmatrix} x \\ y \end{pmatrix} = \begin{pmatrix} 9 \\ 13 \end{pmatrix}$$

The inverse of $\begin{pmatrix} 5 & 2 \\ 7 & 3 \end{pmatrix}$ is $\begin{pmatrix} 3 & -2 \\ -7 & 5 \end{pmatrix}$

Multiplying both sides by the inverse:

$$\begin{pmatrix} 3 & -2 \\ -7 & 5 \end{pmatrix} \begin{pmatrix} 5 & 2 \\ 7 & 3 \end{pmatrix} \begin{pmatrix} x \\ y \end{pmatrix} = \begin{pmatrix} 3 & -2 \\ -7 & 5 \end{pmatrix} \begin{pmatrix} 9 \\ 13 \end{pmatrix}$$

But $\begin{pmatrix} 3 & -2 \\ -7 & 5 \end{pmatrix} \begin{pmatrix} 5 & 2 \\ 7 & 3 \end{pmatrix} = \begin{pmatrix} 1 & 0 \\ 0 & 1 \end{pmatrix}$

therefore $\begin{pmatrix} 1 & 0 \\ 0 & 1 \end{pmatrix} \begin{pmatrix} x \\ y \end{pmatrix} = \begin{pmatrix} 27 - 26 \\ -63 + 65 \end{pmatrix} = \begin{pmatrix} 1 \\ 2 \end{pmatrix}$

therefore $\begin{aligned} x &= 1 \\ y &= 2 \end{aligned}$

It will be noticed that in this example the determinant of the matrix $\begin{pmatrix} 5 & 2 \\ 7 & 3 \end{pmatrix}$ is $15 - 14 = 1$

Let us now take an example where the determinant is not 1.

Example

Solve for x and y

$$\begin{cases} 3x + y = -1 \\ 3x + 2y = 1 \end{cases}$$

Rewriting:

$$\begin{pmatrix} 3 & 1 \\ 3 & 2 \end{pmatrix} \begin{pmatrix} x \\ y \end{pmatrix} = \begin{pmatrix} -1 \\ 1 \end{pmatrix}$$

The inverse of $\begin{pmatrix} 3 & 1 \\ 3 & 2 \end{pmatrix}$ is $\begin{pmatrix} \dfrac{2}{3} & \dfrac{-1}{3} \\ \dfrac{-3}{3} & \dfrac{3}{3} \end{pmatrix}$

Now leave out the denominators in the inverse and use $\frac{1}{3} \begin{pmatrix} 2 & -1 \\ -3 & 3 \end{pmatrix}$

As before multiply both sides of the equation by $\frac{1}{3} \begin{pmatrix} 2 & -1 \\ -3 & 3 \end{pmatrix}$

$$\frac{1}{3} \begin{pmatrix} 2 & -1 \\ -3 & 3 \end{pmatrix} \begin{pmatrix} 3 & 1 \\ 3 & 2 \end{pmatrix} \begin{pmatrix} x \\ y \end{pmatrix} = \frac{1}{3} \begin{pmatrix} 2 & -1 \\ -3 & 3 \end{pmatrix} \begin{pmatrix} -1 \\ 1 \end{pmatrix}$$

We have $\begin{pmatrix} 1 & 0 \\ 0 & 1 \end{pmatrix} \begin{pmatrix} x \\ y \end{pmatrix} = \begin{pmatrix} -2 & -1 \\ 3 & +3 \end{pmatrix} = \begin{pmatrix} -1 \\ 2 \end{pmatrix}$

Therefore $\begin{pmatrix} 1 & 0 \\ 0 & 1 \end{pmatrix} \begin{pmatrix} x \\ y \end{pmatrix} = \begin{pmatrix} -1 \\ 2 \end{pmatrix}$

Hence $\begin{cases} x = -1 \\ y = \ \ 2 \end{cases}$

or A useful general rule is to carry out the procedure ignoring the determinant and, having found the values of x and y, **then** divide these values by the determinant. It is wise to call x and y during the sum x_1 and y_1 until the final line.

Example

Solve $\begin{cases} 4x + y = -5 \\ 3x + 2y = \ \ 0 \end{cases}$

Matrix $= \begin{pmatrix} 4 & 1 \\ 3 & 2 \end{pmatrix}$; the inverse, ignoring the determinant

$$= \begin{pmatrix} 2 & -1 \\ -3 & 4 \end{pmatrix}$$

hence
$$\begin{pmatrix} 2 & -1 \\ -3 & 4 \end{pmatrix} \begin{pmatrix} 4 & 1 \\ 3 & 2 \end{pmatrix} \begin{pmatrix} x_1 \\ y_1 \end{pmatrix}$$
$$= \begin{pmatrix} 2 & -1 \\ -2 & 4 \end{pmatrix} \begin{pmatrix} -5 \\ 0 \end{pmatrix} = \begin{pmatrix} -10 \\ 15 \end{pmatrix}$$

therefore
$$x_1 = -10$$
$$y_1 = \ \ 15$$

The determinant $= 4 \times 2 - 3 \times 1 = 5$

hence $\begin{cases} x = -2 \\ y = \ \ 3 \end{cases}$

EXERCISE No. 17

1. Find all the possible solutions, using matrices, for the following simultaneous equations:

(a) $\begin{cases} 2x + y = 7 \\ 3x + 2y = 12 \end{cases}$

(b) $\begin{cases} 7x - 2y = 4 \\ 11x + 3y = 37 \end{cases}$

(c) $\begin{cases} 2x + y = 1 \\ 4x + 2y = 2 \end{cases}$

(d) $\begin{cases} 4x + 2y = -4 \\ x + y = 0 \end{cases}$

(e) $\begin{cases} 3x + 4y = -3 \\ -x + 6y = 12 \end{cases}$

(f) $\begin{cases} 4x + y = 6 \\ 2x + 3y = -12 \end{cases}$

(g) $\begin{cases} -7x + 3y = 5 \\ x - 2y = -1\frac{1}{2} \end{cases}$

21. A SQUARE 3 BY 3 MATRIX

The principles are the same as for 2 by 2 matrices. The unit matrix is

$$I_3 = \begin{pmatrix} 1 & 0 & 0 \\ 0 & 1 & 0 \\ 0 & 0 & 1 \end{pmatrix} \qquad \text{N.B. } I_1 = (1)$$
$$I_2 = \begin{pmatrix} 1 & 0 \\ 0 & 1 \end{pmatrix}$$

This is now shown to be the unit matrix as follows:

$$\begin{pmatrix} a & b & c \\ d & e & f \\ g & h & i \end{pmatrix} \begin{pmatrix} 1 & 0 & 0 \\ 0 & 1 & 0 \\ 0 & 0 & 1 \end{pmatrix} = \begin{pmatrix} a & b & c \\ d & e & f \\ g & h & i \end{pmatrix}$$

and

$$\begin{pmatrix} 1 & 0 & 0 \\ 0 & 1 & 0 \\ 0 & 0 & 1 \end{pmatrix} \begin{pmatrix} a & b & c \\ d & e & f \\ g & h & i \end{pmatrix} = \begin{pmatrix} a & b & c \\ d & e & f \\ g & h & i \end{pmatrix}$$

EXERCISE No. 18

1. Are the following statements true or false?

(a) The inverse of $\begin{pmatrix} 4 & 0 & 5 \\ 0 & 1 & -6 \\ 3 & 0 & 4 \end{pmatrix}$ is $\begin{pmatrix} 4 & 0 & -5 \\ -18 & 1 & 24 \\ -3 & 0 & 4 \end{pmatrix}$

(b) The inverse of $\begin{pmatrix} 2 & 1 & 0 \\ 3 & 1 & -1 \\ 2 & 5 & 1 \end{pmatrix}$ is $\begin{pmatrix} 2 & 1 & 0 \\ -12 & 1 & -4 \\ -2 & 5 & 1 \end{pmatrix}$

22. TABULATION

The following example illustrates how matrices and matrix multiplication can be used in tabulating data.

Example

Three shops, belonging to the same company, in three different towns, sold on a particular Saturday between 2.0 and 3.0 p.m. the following items:

1st shop: 5 shirts, 3 ties, 4 pairs socks, 3 handkerchiefs, 2 pullovers

2nd shop: 0 shirts, 9 ties, 0 pairs socks, 6 handkerchiefs, 1 pullover

3rd shop: 2 shirts, 4 ties, 8 pairs socks, 4 handkerchiefs, 3 pullovers

(a) This information is written in matrix form, as follows:

	1st shop	2nd shop	3rd shop
Shirts	5	0	2
Ties	3	9	4
Socks	4	0	8
Handkerchiefs	3	6	4
Pullovers	2	1	3

(b) Between 2.0 and 3.0 p.m. on the following Saturday the first shop sold twice the number of each item that it had sold the previous Saturday; the second shop sold the same number and the third shop three times as many.

By matrix multiplication find the total number of each item sold for the two Saturdays.

The matrix

	1st shop	2nd shop	3rd shop
Shirts	5	0	2
Ties	3	9	4
Socks	4	0	8
Handkerchiefs	3	6	4
Pullovers	2	1	3

which has 5 rows and 3 columns [a 5 by 3 matrix] must be multiplied by

1st shop	2
2nd shop	1
3rd shop	3

which has 3 rows and 1 column.

[Remember that two matrices can be multiplied only if there is the same number of columns in the first matrix as rows in the second matrix.]

$$\begin{pmatrix} 5 & 0 & 2 \\ 3 & 9 & 4 \\ 4 & 0 & 8 \\ 3 & 6 & 4 \\ 2 & 1 & 3 \end{pmatrix} \begin{pmatrix} 2 \\ 1 \\ 3 \end{pmatrix} = \begin{matrix} \text{Shirts} \\ \text{Ties} \\ \text{Socks} \\ \text{Handkerchiefs} \\ \text{Pullovers} \end{matrix} \begin{pmatrix} 16 \\ 27 \\ 32 \\ 24 \\ 14 \end{pmatrix}$$

The single-column matrix gives the total number of each item sold by the three shops.

(*c*) The profits on each item are as follows:

Shirts, 8*s*.; Ties, 3*s*.; Socks, 2*s*.; Handkerchiefs, 1*s*.; Pullovers, 12*s*.

Write down the profit vector (matrix), and by matrix multiplication find the profit for each item and the total profit.

$$
\text{The profit vector is}
\begin{array}{l}
\text{Shirts} \\
\text{Ties} \\
\text{Socks} \\
\text{Handkerchiefs} \\
\text{Pullovers}
\end{array}
\overset{\text{shillings}}{\begin{pmatrix} 8 \\ 3 \\ 2 \\ 1 \\ 12 \end{pmatrix}}
$$

The total number of each item sold is written as a 1-row 5-column matrix and multiplied by the profit matrix as follows:

$$
\begin{array}{ccccc}
\text{Shirts} & \text{Ties} & \text{Socks} & \text{Handkerchiefs} & \text{Pullovers} \\
(16 & 27 & 32 & 24 & 14)
\end{array}
\begin{pmatrix} 8 \\ 3 \\ 2 \\ 1 \\ 12 \end{pmatrix}
\begin{array}{l}
\text{Profit in shillings} \\[2pt]
\text{Shirts} \\
\text{Ties} \\
\text{Socks} \\
\text{Handkerchiefs} \\
\text{Pullovers}
\end{array}
$$

$$= (16 \times 8 + 27 \times 3 + 32 \times 2 + 24 \times 1 + 14 \times 12) \text{ shillings}$$
$$= 465 \text{ shillings} = £23\ 5s.$$

N.B. In tabulation examples it is important to write the matrices in such a way that matrix multiplication is possible (see paragraph 19).

EXERCISE No. 19

1. Three housewives made the following purchases:

Mrs "A" bought 2 lb. apples, 3 lb. bananas, 1 cucumber

Mrs "B" bought 1 lb. apples, 2 lb. tomatoes, 2 cucumbers, 1 lettuce

Mrs "C" bought 1 lb. tomatoes, $\frac{1}{2}$ cucumber, 2 lettuces, 2 lb. bananas

(*a*) Write down each of their purchases as row vectors. [Let the 3 rows be Mrs "A", Mrs "B", Mrs "C".] Apples are 6*d*. per lb.; bananas 1*s*. 6*d*. per lb.; cucumbers, 2*s*. each; tomatoes 2*s*. 6*d*. per lb.; and lettuce 1*s*. each.

(*b*) Multiply the matrix from (*a*) by the price column vector and find each of the housewives' greengrocery bill.

2. A coal merchant received the following orders:

Mr Smith ordered: 5 cwt. coal; 16 cwt. anthracite; 1 load of logs; 4 cwt. coke

Mr Jones ordered: 2 cwt. coal; 2 loads of logs; 1 ton coke

Mr Brown ordered 12 cwt. anthracite; 10 cwt. coke; 1 load of logs

Mr West ordered 2 cwt. coke; 8 cwt. anthracite; 10 cwt. coal

  (i) Write this information in matrix form.
 (ii) Find the total quantities of each type of fuel that the merchant has to supply.
(iii) Find the total weight of fuel supplied, excluding logs.
        Coal is 11s. per cwt.; anthracite 16s. 6d. per cwt.; coke 14s. per cwt.; logs £2 per load; and the merchant charges 1s. per cwt. delivery charge but no extra charge for delivering logs.
 (iv) Write down the price vector, and by matrix multiplication find the cost of each order in pounds and shillings.
  (v) Find the total receipts of the merchant for these orders.

3. Christmas hampers are made up as follows:

No. 1 contains 1 Christmas pudding, 1 bottle of sherry, 1 box of crackers

No. 2 contains 2 Christmas puddings, 1 bottle each of sherry and brandy, 1 box of crackers

No. 3 contains 2 Christmas puddings, 1 box of cigars, 1 bottle of brandy, 2 bottles of sherry, 2 boxes of crackers.

No. 4 contains 2 boxes of cigars, 2 bottles of brandy.

  (i) Tabulate this information in matrix form.
 (ii) An order is received from a retailer for 5 No. 1 hampers, 2 of No. 2, 10 of No. 3 and 1 of No. 4. By multiplying by the appropriate vector, find out how many of the various items are needed to meet the order.
(iii) The prices are as follows: Christmas puddings 8s.; sherry 15s. per bottle; brandy 40s. per bottle; cigars 20s. per box; crackers 4s. 6d. per box.
        Write down the price vector and by suitable multiplication find the cost of the whole order.

                                      [O. and C. "O" level, July 1964]

23. Matrices may be introduced via geometrical transformations, and although this has not been the approach here, nevertheless geometrical transformations are important, and some of the simple ideas are dealt with in the following paragraphs:

(a) A vector quantity has magnitude and direction, e.g. the line $\overrightarrow{OA}$ can be represented as follows:

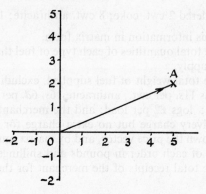

The magnitude of $\overrightarrow{OA} = \sqrt{25 + 4} = \sqrt{29}$ and the direction is given as well.

The co-ordinates of A are $x = 5$, $y = 2$ which can be written as a column vector as follows: $\begin{pmatrix} 5 \\ 2 \end{pmatrix}$

(b) Addition

If $x = 2$ and $y = 3$, i.e. $\begin{pmatrix} 2 \\ 3 \end{pmatrix}$, is added to $x = 1$, $y = 4$, i.e. $\begin{pmatrix} 1 \\ 4 \end{pmatrix}$,

then $\begin{pmatrix} 2 \\ 3 \end{pmatrix} + \begin{pmatrix} 1 \\ 4 \end{pmatrix} = \begin{pmatrix} 3 \\ 7 \end{pmatrix}$

and this can be represented as follows:

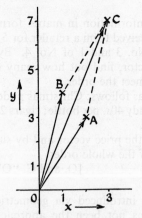

$\overrightarrow{OA}$ represents $\begin{pmatrix} 2 \\ 3 \end{pmatrix}$, $\overrightarrow{OB}$ represents $\begin{pmatrix} 1 \\ 4 \end{pmatrix}$

and $\qquad \overrightarrow{OC}$ represents the sum of $\overrightarrow{OA}$ and $\overrightarrow{OB}$

where $\qquad \overrightarrow{OC}$ is the column vector $\begin{pmatrix} 3 \\ 7 \end{pmatrix}$

(c) Scalar multiplication (see paragraph 11(b)).

(d) Matrix representation of mapping

$$A = \begin{pmatrix} 2 \\ 4 \end{pmatrix} \quad \text{then} \quad \begin{pmatrix} 2 & 1 \\ 3 & 2 \end{pmatrix} \begin{pmatrix} 2 \\ 4 \end{pmatrix} = \begin{pmatrix} 8 \\ 14 \end{pmatrix} = B$$

$A \begin{pmatrix} 2 \\ 4 \end{pmatrix}$ has been mapped or transformed into $B \begin{pmatrix} 8 \\ 14 \end{pmatrix}$ as is shown below:

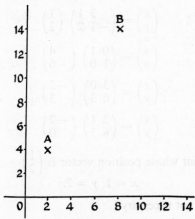

The matrix multiplication has moved (mapped or transformed) A to B.

CLASS DISCUSSION QUESTION

[O. and C. "O" Level, 1964]

The position vector of a point whose co-ordinates are (x, y) is written as the column matrix $\begin{pmatrix} x \\ y \end{pmatrix}$.

(a) If

$$\begin{pmatrix} x' \\ y' \end{pmatrix} = A \begin{pmatrix} x \\ y \end{pmatrix}, \text{ where } A = \begin{pmatrix} 1 & 0 \\ 0 & -1 \end{pmatrix},$$

show on a diagram the points (x, y) and (x', y') and describe the geometrical transformation of which A is the matrix.

(b) In a new diagram show the position of a point (x, y) in the first quadrant and the end-point (X, Y) of the vector obtained by rotating the position vector of (x, y) anticlockwise through a quarter-turn. Write down the equations connecting (x, y) and (X, Y), and hence find the matrix, B, of this transformation.

(c) Calculate the matrix products AB and BA.

(d) Plot the points P and Q into which $(5, 3)$ goes under the transformations given by AB and BA respectively, and find the equation of the line in which P is the reflection of Q.

EXERCISE No. 20

1. Calculate x and y for the following:

(i) $$\begin{pmatrix} x \\ y \end{pmatrix} = \begin{pmatrix} 3 & 1 \\ -1 & 2 \end{pmatrix} \begin{pmatrix} 1 \\ 2 \end{pmatrix}$$

(ii) $$\begin{pmatrix} x \\ y \end{pmatrix} = \begin{pmatrix} 0 & 1 \\ 1 & 0 \end{pmatrix} \begin{pmatrix} 4 \\ -6 \end{pmatrix}$$

(iii) $$\begin{pmatrix} x \\ y \end{pmatrix} = \begin{pmatrix} 3 & 0 \\ 0 & 3 \end{pmatrix} \begin{pmatrix} -2 \\ 3 \end{pmatrix}$$

(iv) $$\begin{pmatrix} x \\ y \end{pmatrix} = \begin{pmatrix} 2 & 1 \\ 6 & 3 \end{pmatrix} \begin{pmatrix} -2 \\ 0 \end{pmatrix}$$

2. Plot the point whose position vector is $\begin{pmatrix} 1 \\ 2 \end{pmatrix}$,

i.e. $$x = 1, y = 2.$$

[Graph paper is not necessary.]

Plot the points whose position vectors are given by the following transformations:

(a) $\begin{pmatrix} 0 & 1 \\ 1 & 0 \end{pmatrix} \begin{pmatrix} 1 \\ 2 \end{pmatrix}$ (b) $\begin{pmatrix} 0 & 2 \\ 2 & 0 \end{pmatrix} \begin{pmatrix} 1 \\ 2 \end{pmatrix}$

(c) $\begin{pmatrix} 1 & -1 \\ 0 & 1 \end{pmatrix} \begin{pmatrix} 1 \\ 2 \end{pmatrix}$ (d) $\begin{pmatrix} -2 & 6 \\ 1 & -3 \end{pmatrix} \begin{pmatrix} 1 \\ 2 \end{pmatrix}$

3. Can the transformations of Question 2 be reversed?

4. Plot the points corresponding to the vectors

$$\begin{pmatrix} 1 \\ 2 \end{pmatrix}; \begin{pmatrix} 1 \\ 3 \end{pmatrix}; \begin{pmatrix} -1 \\ 2 \end{pmatrix}; \begin{pmatrix} -1 \\ -2 \end{pmatrix}; \begin{pmatrix} 0 \\ 0 \end{pmatrix}; \begin{pmatrix} 1 \\ 1 \end{pmatrix}$$

under the transformation given by the matrix

$$\begin{pmatrix} -2 & 6 \\ 1 & -3 \end{pmatrix}$$

5. Can the transformations of Question 4 be reversed?

6. Find x and y if:

(a) $(x, y) \begin{pmatrix} 3 & 0 \\ -3 & 2 \end{pmatrix} = (12, 12)$

(b) $(x, y) \begin{pmatrix} 4 & -2 \\ 0 & 3 \end{pmatrix} = (8, 11)$

(c) $\begin{pmatrix} -1 & 1 \\ 0 & -2 \end{pmatrix} \begin{pmatrix} x \\ y \end{pmatrix} = \begin{pmatrix} 3 \\ -6 \end{pmatrix}$

(d) $\begin{pmatrix} 7 & 0 \\ -4 & 5 \end{pmatrix} \begin{pmatrix} x \\ y \end{pmatrix} = \begin{pmatrix} 21 \\ 18 \end{pmatrix}$

24. SOLUTION OF 3 EQUATIONS WITH 3 UNKNOWNS

The method described in the following example is included here, as it is an introduction to the method for solving linear programming problems of the type dealt with in the second half of the linear programming chapter.

An inverse method similar to that for 2 by 2 matrices could be used, but the method now described is important, as it is more general.

Example

Solve for x, y and z

$$\begin{cases} x + y + z = 2 \\ 2x - 2y + 3z = 2 \\ 3x - y - z = -6 \end{cases}$$

Rewrite:

$$\begin{pmatrix} 1 & 1 & 1 \\ 2 & -2 & 3 \\ 3 & -1 & -1 \end{pmatrix} \begin{pmatrix} x \\ y \\ z \end{pmatrix} = \begin{pmatrix} 2 \\ 2 \\ -6 \end{pmatrix}$$

The aim is to end up with a number in each column and 2 zeros. This is done by adding or subtracting multiples of a row to the other 2 rows as follows:

(i) Multiply the first row by 2 and subtract it from the second row—leaving the third row untouched.

$$\begin{pmatrix} 1 & 1 & 1 \\ 2-2 & -2-2 & 3-2 \end{pmatrix} \begin{pmatrix} x \\ y \\ z \end{pmatrix} = \begin{pmatrix} 2 \\ 2-4 \end{pmatrix}$$

At the same time multiply the first row by 3 and subtract it from the third row.

$$\begin{pmatrix} 1 & 1 & 1 \\ 2-2 & -2-2 & 3-2 \\ 3-3 & -1-3 & -1-3 \end{pmatrix} \begin{pmatrix} x \\ y \\ z \end{pmatrix} = \begin{pmatrix} 2 \\ 2-4 \\ -6-6 \end{pmatrix}$$

which becomes

$$\begin{pmatrix} 1 & 1 & 1 \\ 0 & -4 & +1 \\ 0 & -4 & -4 \end{pmatrix} \begin{pmatrix} x \\ y \\ z \end{pmatrix} = \begin{pmatrix} 2 \\ -2 \\ -12 \end{pmatrix}$$

In the 1st column we now have a real number in the first row and zeros in the 2nd and 3rd rows.

(ii) Operating on the 2nd row. Write down the 2nd row as it stands. Multiply the 1st row by 4 and add the 2nd row to it. For the 3rd row subtract the 2nd row from it.

$$\begin{pmatrix} 4 & 4-4 & 4+1 \\ 0 & -4 & +1 \\ 0 & -4+4 & -4-1 \end{pmatrix} \begin{pmatrix} x \\ y \\ z \end{pmatrix} = \begin{pmatrix} 8-2 \\ -2 \\ -12+2 \end{pmatrix}$$

which becomes

$$\begin{pmatrix} 4 & 0 & 5 \\ 0 & -4 & +1 \\ 0 & 0 & -5 \end{pmatrix} \begin{pmatrix} x \\ y \\ z \end{pmatrix} = \begin{pmatrix} 6 \\ -2 \\ -10 \end{pmatrix}$$

We now have in the 2nd column one number and two zeros.

(iii) Operating on the 3rd row. Write down the 3rd row as it stands. Add the third row to the first. Multiply the 2nd row by 5 and add the 3rd row to it.

$$\begin{pmatrix} 4 & 0 & 0 \\ 0 & -20 & +5-5 \\ 0 & 0 & -5 \end{pmatrix} \begin{pmatrix} x \\ y \\ z \end{pmatrix} = \begin{pmatrix} -4 \\ -10-10 \\ -10 \end{pmatrix}$$

which becomes

$$\begin{pmatrix} 4 & 0 & 0 \\ 0 & -20 & 0 \\ 0 & 0 & -5 \end{pmatrix} \begin{pmatrix} x \\ y \\ z \end{pmatrix} = \begin{pmatrix} -4 \\ -20 \\ -10 \end{pmatrix}$$

(iv) The left-hand side when multiplied out becomes

$$\begin{pmatrix} 4x \\ -20y \\ -5z \end{pmatrix}$$

and the right-hand side is $\begin{pmatrix} -4 \\ -20 \\ -10 \end{pmatrix}$

$$\Rightarrow \begin{cases} 4x = -4 \\ -20y = -20 \\ -5z = -10 \end{cases} \Rightarrow \begin{cases} x = -1 \\ y = 1 \\ z = 2 \end{cases}$$

EXERCISE No. 21

1. Solve the following simultaneous equation for x, y and z, using the method explained in paragraph 24.

(a) $\begin{cases} 2x + 5z = 12 \\ y - 3z = -7 \\ 3x + z = 5 \end{cases}$

(b) $\begin{cases} x + 2y + z = 3 \\ 2x - 3z = -13 \\ x + 3y + 2z = 7 \end{cases}$

(c) $\begin{cases} 2x - y + z = 8 \\ x - 3y - 2z = -1 \\ 5x + y - 3z = 0 \end{cases}$

2. $\begin{cases} -4x + 3y = P \\ 5x - 4y = Q \\ -3x + 2y = R \end{cases}$

What is the equation connecting P, Q and R for the above equations to have a solution?

3. Is there a solution for x, y, z for the following equations?:

$$\begin{cases} 2x - y + z = 8 \\ x - 3y - 2z = -1 \\ 4x + 3y + 2z = 26 \end{cases}$$

Chapter 6

LINEAR PROGRAMMING

1. L. V. Kantorovich and his colleagues in Russia in 1939 and G. B. Dantzig and his colleagues in the U.S.A. in 1947 needed to solve a set of linear equations which arose from military problems. The Americans did not know of the Russians' work, and they developed a procedure for solving such equations. These procedures have since been adapted to help solve business problems, and where many equations are involved a computer is used.

2. Before discussing a linear programming problem we will summarise the symbols that will be used.

(a) Inequalities

$$\begin{cases} x > y \\ x \text{ is greater than } y \end{cases} \qquad \begin{cases} x < y \\ x \text{ is less than } y \end{cases}$$

$$\begin{cases} x \geqslant y \\ x \text{ is greater than or equal to } y \end{cases} \qquad \begin{cases} x \leqslant y \\ x \text{ is less than or equal to } y \end{cases}$$

Examples

   (i) $3 > 2$

   (ii) $-4 < -1$

   (iii) $x \leqslant 3$, means that x can have any value less than and including 3, e.g. $x = -7$, $1\cdot5$, 3, **but** x cannot have any value greater than 3.

(b) A linear equation of the type

$$Ax + By + C = 0$$

where A, B and C are any numbers

represents the locus of all points whose co-ordinates (x, y) satisfy the equation.

The line $3x + 2y = 6$, for example, is represented as follows:

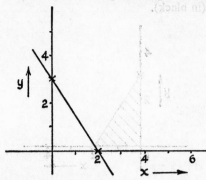

The following points lie on the line:

$$x = 0\} \quad x = 2\} \quad x = 1\}$$
$$y = 3\} \quad y = 0\} \quad y = 1{\cdot}5\} \text{ etc.}$$

(c) Consider the inequality

$$3x + 2y < 6$$

All points in the shaded area satisfy this inequality, but no points on the boundary line itself are included.

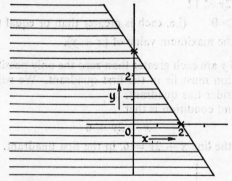

The shaded area is called an

OPEN HALF PLANE

(d) For the inequality

$$3x + 2y \leqslant 6$$

all points in the shaded area, **including** all points on the line itself, satisfy the condition. This is called a CLOSED HALF PLANE and consists of an open half plane together with its boundary.

(e)
$$\begin{cases} x \geqslant 0 \\ y \geqslant 0 \\ 3x + 2y \leqslant 6 \end{cases}$$

G

All points in the shaded area satisfy these conditions, including the boundary lines (in black).

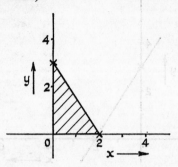

3. To begin with, problems involving only two variables, excluding the slack variables, will be considered, as these can be done graphically. (See Para. 5.1.)

GRAPHICAL REPRESENTATION
Problem

$$x + 2y \leqslant 6$$
$$3x + 2y \leqslant 12$$
$$x, y \geqslant 0 \qquad \text{(i.e. each is greater than or equal to zero)}$$

Find the maximum value of $(x + y)$.

(i) As x and y are each greater than zero the only possible values of the solution must lie in the first quadrant. We will, therefore, only consider this quadrant.
(ii) The second condition is that

$$x + 2y \leqslant 6$$

Draw the line $x + 2y = 6$, in the first quadrant.

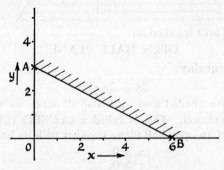

AB is the line $x + 2y = 6$

The inequality $x + 2y \leqslant 6$ means that all points on the line AB and within the area OAB are possible, and none outside. Hence AB is the boundary, and **no** points in the shaded area are possible.

(iii) The third condition is that $3x + 2y \leqslant 12$

Draw the line $3x + 2y = 12$.

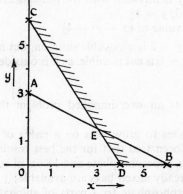

DC is the line $3x + 2y = 12$. The inequality $3x + 2y \leqslant 12$ means that points on the line CD within the area OCD are possible. The shaded area represents impossible points. The two conditions, however, leave as the feasible area only $OAED$. Any points on the boundary and within this area are possible.

(iv) Our problem was to find the maximum value of $(x + y)$.

Let $x + y = n$, where n has any positive value, e.g. $\frac{1}{2}$, 1, $1\frac{1}{2}$, 2, etc.

If we draw on the graph lines for
$$x + y = 2, \ x + y = 4\tfrac{1}{2}, \ x + y = 6$$
we see that they are all parallel to each other.

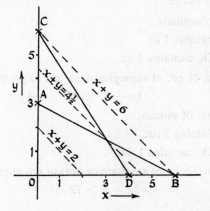

The furthest line from the origin to contain a point satisfying the condition that it must lie within the area $OAED$ is the line

$$x + y = 4\tfrac{1}{2}$$

Hence the maximum value that $(x + y)$ can have is $4\tfrac{1}{2}$. This line passes through E, which is on the boundary but is possible. The boundary is included with the possible area $OAED$.

At E, $x = 3$, $y = 1\tfrac{1}{2}$

Maximum value of $(x + y) = 4\tfrac{1}{2}$

N.B. $x + y = 2$ is a possible solution, but not the maximum value. $x + y = 6$ is **not** possible, as it is outside the area $OAED$.

4. EXAMPLE

The following is an oversimplified problem that can be done graphically.

A gardener wishes to grow peas on a patch of land 6 yards by 8 yards. He has been told that for the best results on his land he needs at least 1 oz. superphosphate and $1\tfrac{1}{2}$ oz. of sulphate of potash per sq. yd. Two ready mixed bags are available; $\tfrac{1}{4}$ lb. of GRO contains 1 part superphosphate to 3 parts of sulphate of potash and costs 2s. $\tfrac{1}{4}$ lb. of QUICK contains 3 parts of superphosphate to 1 part of sulphate of potash and costs 3s. How many bags of GRO and QUICK should the gardener buy in order to meet his requirements for the least cost?

Let $x = $ No. of bags of GRO

Let $y = $ No. of bags of QUICK

(i) $x \geqslant 0, y \geqslant 0$ [as we cannot take the fertilizer out of the ground]

(ii) Requirement of superphosphate $= 6 \times 8 \times 1$ oz. $= 48$ oz.

Requirement of sulphate of potash $= 6 \times 8 \times \tfrac{3}{2}$ oz. $= 72$ oz.

The inequalities are

(iii) For superphosphate;

GRO contains 1 oz.

and QUICK contains 3 oz.

and at least 48 oz. of superphosphate are required.

Thus $1x + 3y \geqslant 48$

(iv) For sulphate of potash;

GRO contains 3 oz.

and QUICK contains 1 oz.

and at least 72 oz. of sulphate of potash are required

Thus $3x + y \geqslant 72$

(v) Cost $= 2x + 3y$ (in shillings)

and this is to be a **minimum**

$\therefore$ Let $2x + 3y = C$

The problem is then to find the minimum value of C.

Solution

Draw the line $x + 3y = 48$ (*AB* on the graph)

Draw the line $3x + y = 72$ (*CD* on the graph)

Let these lines meet at E.

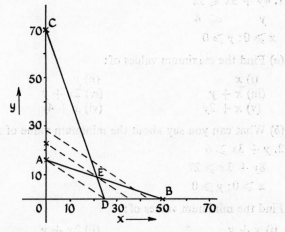

As $x + 3y \geqslant 48$ and $3x + y \geqslant 72$, no points inside the area $OCEB$ are possible.

The cost equation is

$$2x + 3y = C \qquad \text{or} \qquad y = -\frac{2}{3}x + \frac{C}{3}$$

where C has any positive value.

Let $C = 48$, 69 and 84

The lines $\begin{cases} 2x + 3y = 48 \\ 2x + 3y = 69 \\ 2x + 3y = 84 \end{cases}$

are seen to be parallel to each other.

The first line $2x + 3y = 48$ is in the infeasible area; the second passes through the point $x = 21$, $y = 9$, which is on the boundary and possible; the third $2x + 3y = 84$ although possible is not the cheapest.

Hence the optimal (best) solution occurs at E, where $x = 21$ and $y = 9$. The minimum cost is then,

$$C = 69 \text{ shillings}$$

The gardener should buy 21 bags of GRO and 9 bags of QUICK for a total cost of £3 9s.

N.B. The intersection of the two lines does not necessarily indicate the optimal solution.

EXERCISE No. 22

1. $4y + 3x \leqslant 32$

     $y \quad\quad \leqslant 4$

     $x \geqslant 0;\; y \geqslant 0$

(a) Find the maximum values of:

    (i) x (ii) y

    (iii) $x + y$ (iv) $2x + y$

    (v) $x + 2y$ (vi) $x + 4y$

(b) What can you say about the minimum value of $x + y$?

2. $y + 3x \geqslant 6$

     $8y + 3x \geqslant 27$

     $x \geqslant 0;\; y \geqslant 0$

Find the minimum values of:

    (i) $x + y$ (ii) $2x + y$

    (iii) $x + 2y$ (iv) $x + 3y$

    (v) $x + 4y$ (vi) $8x + y$

3. $3x - y \leqslant 6$

     $2x + 3y \leqslant 26$

     $x + 4y \leqslant 18$

     $x \geqslant 0;\; y \geqslant 0$

Find the maximum values of:

    (i) $x + y$ (ii) $2x + y$ (iii) $x + 2y$

    (iv) $3x + y$ (v) $x + 3y$

4. $2x + y \geqslant 5$

     $x + y \geqslant 4$

     $x + 3y \geqslant 6$

     $x \geqslant 0;\; y \geqslant 0$

Find the minimum values of

(i) $3x + y$ (ii) $3x + 2y$ (iii) $x + 5y$

5. $x \geqslant 4$

     $2x + y \geqslant 22$

     $x + 4y \geqslant 32$

     $7x + 10y \leqslant 188$

Find minimum **and** maximum values of:

(i) $x + y$ (ii) $3x + y$ (iii) $x + 3y$

(iv) $7x + 2y$ (v) $x + 7y$

6. A firm making motor cars produces two types, estate and de luxe. The profit on estate cars is £30 per car and on de luxe cars £50 per car. Estate cars are assembled in 20 hours and painted in 10 hours. De luxe cars are assembled in 30 hours and painted in 20 hours. There are 1,200 hours available for assembly and 700 hours available for painting. How many of each type of car should the firm make for maximum profit if they can sell all that they can make of either type?

7. A seedsman has stocks of two chemicals A and B. He can mix these in the ratio 3 parts of A to 1 part of B to produce a general fertiliser; or in the ratio 1 part of A to 3 parts of B to produce a tomato fertiliser. He sells these fertilisers in 1-lb. bags, making $3d$. per lb. profit on the former, and $6d$. per lb. profit on the latter.

Given that he makes x lb. of general fertiliser and y lb. of tomato fertiliser, and that he has only 60 lb. of A in stock, write down an inequality satisfied by x and y.

Write down a second inequality, given that the stock of B is 30 lb., and use a graphical method to find the values of x and y to maximise his profit. Hence find his maximum profit.

[O. and C. "O" level July 1964]

8. A boy goes out with 5s. in his pocket to buy fireworks. He buys x rockets at $6d$. each and y crackers at $3d$. each. Write down the total cost of these in pence. If he does not spend all his money, write down an inequality connecting x and y.

He has promised to buy at least 4 rockets, but has also decided to buy more than twice as many crackers as rockets. Express both these statements as inequalities.

On suitable axes graph the three inequalities, making clear which areas are relevant. Hence determine the ordered pairs (x, y) expressing his possible purchases. [O. and C., "O" level July 1964]

9. Doctor N. It, claims that he can cure colds with his new 3-part pills, These come in 2 sizes: "Standard" size containing 2 grains of

aspirin, 5 grains of arsenic and 1 grain of codein; "KILL" size containing 1 grain of aspirin, 8 grains of arsenic and 6 grains of codein. His research has convinced him that it requires at least 12 grains of aspirin, 74 grains of arsenic and 28 grains of codein to effect his desired "result"! Determine the least number of pills he should prescribe in order to meet these requirements.

10. $x_1 - 2x_2 + 20 \geqslant 0$

$x_1 + 4x_2 \qquad \leqslant 52$

$x_1 + x_2 \qquad \leqslant 19$

$x_1 \qquad \leqslant 12$

$x_1 - 2x_2 \qquad \leqslant 6$

Find graphically the intersections of the above inequalities, and hence find the maximum value of $x_1 + 3x_2$.

5. SIMPLEX METHOD

A procedure for solving simultaneous linear equations that is easily adapted to computers is the simplex method.

A simple example will be worked to show the procedure.

Example

Find the maximum value of $8x_1 + 6x_2$ if

$$2x_1 + 3x_2 \leqslant 10$$
$$2x_1 + x_2 \leqslant 6$$
$$x_1 \geqslant 0, x_2 \geqslant 0$$

(i) The inequalities are changed to equations by the introduction of "slack" variables y_1 and y_2. [Slack variables must be non-negative.]

Hence

$$2x_1 + 3x_2 + y_1 \qquad = 10$$
$$2x_1 + x_2 \qquad + y_2 = 6$$
$$P = 8x_1 + 6x_2$$

(ii) Before putting these equations into matrix form they are rearranged as follows, with the slack variables on the left-hand sides of the equations:

$$y_1 = 10 - (2x_1 + 3x_2)$$
$$y_2 = 6 - (2x_1 + x_2)$$
$$P = 0 - (-8x_1 - 6x_2)$$

(iii) This is then put into "matrix" form thus:

Labels	Q	x_1	x_2	y_1	y_2
y_1	10	2	3	1	
y_2	6	2	1		1
P	0	-8	-6		

If the variables x_1, x_2 had been given the value zero, then a feasible solution is

$y_1 = 10$, $y_2 = 6$, which gives zero profit

To decide whether x_1 or x_2 should be considered **look at the** "P" row, often called the "CONTROL ROW", for **the "most negative"** value, in this case, -8, then this is the "PIVOT COLUMN".

The profit equation shows that increase of the x_1 value by unity will increase the profit by 8, i.e.

$$P = -(-8 - 0) = +8 \text{ (leaving } x_2 \text{ zero)}$$

x_1 can be increased until one of the independent terms (y_1 and y_2) becomes zero. The limit is found by dividing the Q column by the pivot column as follows:

$$Q/x_1$$
$$y_1 \quad 5$$
$$y_2 \quad 3$$

The minimum positive value gives the limit, i.e. 3

The rows have been labelled y_1, y_2, and these are included in the columns, giving a unit matrix.

(iv) This must appear a cumbersome way of eliminating one variable, in this case, x_1, from one equation, but it must be stressed that the process is iterative and can be done by a computer.

Next,

Divide the y_2 row by 2 to make the x_1 value 1 (digit). The row y_2, is re-labelled x_1

	Q	x_1	x_2	y_1	y_2
x_1	3	1	$\frac{1}{2}$	—	$\frac{1}{2}$

Next,

Eliminate x_1 from the first row by subtracting twice the new second row from the first row, as follows:

New first row

		Q	x_1	x_2	y_1	y_2
i.e.	y_1	$10 - 6$	$2 - 2$	$3 - 1$	$1 - 0$	$0 - 1$
	y_1	4	0	2	1	-1

Next,

Eliminate x_1 from the control row by adding 8 times the new Pivot row to the control row as follows:

	Q	x_1	x_2	y_1	y_2
P	24	0	-2	0	4

The complete tableau at this stage has become:

	Q	x_1	x_2	y_1	y_2	Ratio Q/x_2
y_1	4	0	$2\,^*$	1	-1	$4/2 = 2$
x_1	3	1	$\frac{1}{2}$		$\frac{1}{2}$	$3/\frac{1}{2} = 6$
P	24	0	-2		4	

* Pivot

(v) To eliminate x_2 divide Q by x_2, and the minimum positive value is seen to be 2; as before, divide this row to make x_2 unity and re-label the row x_2

	Q	x_1	x_2	y_1	y_2
x_2	2	0	1	$\frac{1}{2}$	$-\frac{1}{2}$

Next,

Eliminate x_2 from the x_1 row by subtracting half the new row from the x_1 row

	Q	x_1	x_2	y_1	y_2
x_1	2	1	0	$-\frac{1}{4}$	$3/4$

Next,

Eliminate x_2 from the control row by adding twice the pivot row to the control row

	Q	x_1	x_2	y_1	y_2
P	28	0	0	1	3

The final tableau is

	Q	x_1	x_2	y_1	y_2
x_2	2	0	1	$\frac{1}{2}$	$-\frac{1}{2}$
x_1	2	1	0	$-\frac{1}{4}$	$\frac{3}{4}$
P	28	0	0	1	3

(vi) Hence the maximum value of $8x_1 + 6x_2 = 28$

(vii) The penalties on the slack variables y_1 and y_2 are 1 and 3, and in a real example must be taken into account, but in this simplified problem can be ignored.

6. The Rules for the simplex method can be summarised as follows:

(i) Choose the highest numerical negative value in the control row. This gives the pivot column.

(ii) Form the ratio of the Q column divided term by term by the pivot column.

(iii) Choose the lowest positive ratio value. This defines the pivot row.

(iv) Divide the pivot row by the term in the pivot column.

(v) For each other row in the matrix multiply the new pivot row by the element in the pivot column and subtract the result from the row being changed. Do this for every row in the tableau, including the control row.

(vi) If there are still negative values in the control row repeat from number one. When the control row is all positive the solution has been reached.

N.B. As a check on the calculations it is possible to carry an additional column on the matrix which is the sum of all the elements in each row. This column is altered according to the rules above, but the new values should equal the sum of the new row elements.

The following example illustrates the use of the Simplex method in finding the minimum value of a function. The minimisation is replaced by the maximisation of the numerical value of a negative quantity.

Example

$$2y_1 + 2y_2 \geqslant 8$$

$$3y_1 + y_2 \geqslant 6$$

$$y_1 \geqslant 0, y_2 \geqslant 0$$

Find the minimum value of $(10y_1 + 6y_2)$

i.e. the maximum of $(-10y_1 - 6y_2)$

First multiply equations by -1 as follows:

$$-2y_1 - 2y_2 \leqslant -8$$

$$-3y_1 - y_2 \leqslant -6$$

Let the slack variables be x_1 and x_2: they will be positive.

$$- 2y_1 - 2y_2 + x_1 = -8$$

$$- 3y_1 - y_2 + x_2 = -6$$

$$-10y_1 - 6y_2 \qquad -P$$

Rearrange as follows:

$$x_1 = -8 - (-2y_1 - 2y_2)$$

$$x_2 = -6 - (-3y_1 - y_2)$$

$$-P = 0 - (10y_1 + 6y_2)$$

If we let y_1 and y_2 equal zero, x_1 and x_2 are negative, which is not allowed. This corresponds to the infeasible region, as can be checked if the y_1, y_2 graph is drawn. The point $y_1 = 0$, $y_2 = 0$ is infeasible.

Labels	Q	y_1	y_2	x_1	x_2	Ratio
x_1	-8	-2	-2	1		$\dfrac{-8}{-2} = 4$
x_2	-6	-3	-1		1	$\dfrac{-6}{-3} = 2$
$-P$	0	10	6			

There is no negative in the P row, but the negative values in Q must be eliminated, hence choose either y_1 or y_2. Take y_1. In this case the highest positive ratio associated with a negative Q is used to choose the pivot, as this will eliminate as many negative Q values as possible in one iteration. The matrix becomes as follows:

Labels	Q	y_1	y_2	x_1	x_2	Ratio
y_1	4	1	1	$-\frac{1}{2}$		$\frac{4}{1} = 4$
x_2	6	0	2*	$-1\frac{1}{2}$	1	$\frac{6}{2} = 3$
$-P$	-40	0	-4	5		

* New pivot

Now the matrix has all positive Q values and we can proceed as before.

Labels	Q	y_1	y_2	x_1	x_2
y_1	1	1	0	$-\frac{1}{4}$	$-\frac{1}{2}$
y_2	3	0	1	$-\frac{3}{4}$	$\frac{1}{2}$
$-P$	-28	0	0	2	2

Hence $y_1 = 1$, $y_2 = 3$ and $10y_1 + 6y_2 = 28$ give the minimal value.

EXERCISE No. 23

1. Use the Simplex method in the following examples:

(a) $3x_1 + 5x_2 \leqslant 45$

$6x_1 + x_2 \leqslant 36$

$x_1 \geqslant 0; x_2 \geqslant 0$

Find the maximum value of $3x_1 + 4x_2$

(b) $x_1 + 3x_2 \geqslant 6$

$8x_1 + 3x_2 \geqslant 27$

$x_1 \geqslant 0; x_2 \geqslant 0$

Find the minimum value of $x_1 + 2x_2$

(c) $x_1 + 3x_2 \geqslant 18$

$2x_1 + x_2 \geqslant 16$

$x_1 \geqslant 0; x_2 \geqslant 0$

Find the minimum value of $3x_1 + 4x_2$

(d) $x_1 + x_2 + x_3 \leqslant 100$

$3x_1 + 2x_2 + 4x_3 \leqslant 210$

$3x_1 + 2x_2 \qquad \leqslant 150$

Find the maximum value of $5x_1 + 4x_2 + 6x_3$

2. Solve the equations:

$$2x_1 - x_2 + x_3 \qquad + x_5 = 7$$

$$x_1 + 2x_2 + 3x_3 + 3x_4 \qquad = 2$$

$$x_1 \qquad + x_3 - x_4 + 2x_5 = 8$$

Subject to the condition that all x_i must be positive or zero ($i = 1$ to 5).

Prove that there is only one possible solution to this problem.

The simplex method applied to a simple industrial problem is shown in the following example:

Example

A man has a small factory in which he operates a single plastics moulding machine to produce three types of article which he designates A, B and C. The type B is twice the size of each of the other two types. He can connect the moulds to the machine in three different combinations; $1A$ and $2B$; $2A$ and $3C$; or $1A$, $1B$ and $2C$; and no other combination is possible, due to the connections available on the machine. He rents the machine for £2 an hour, and the moulds are rented at £1, £6 and £3 per hour for the types A, B and C respectively, these rents only being payable for the periods for which the mould or machine is in use. In the terms for the rental he is limited to 8 hours' use of the machine per day in a 5-day week. In addition, he pays a rental of £80 per week for the factory site.

The raw material is fed to the machine at a constant rate for all mould combinations and costs £5 for the feed for one hour. Each mould produces 10 articles per hour.

After a study of the market conditions it is found that up to 450 As, 550 Bs and 450 Cs can be sold each week at the current prices of 12s., 16s. and 8s. each, respectively.

How should the man run his machine in order to maximise the profits made, and what is this weekly profit?

Consider a single day's production, and work in batches of 10 articles.

Let C_2 = unknown number of hours worked with 1st combination

Let C_3 = unknown number of hours worked with 2nd combination

Let C_4 = unknown number of hours worked with 3rd combination

For the production of A:

$$1C_2 + 2C_3 + 1C_4 \leqslant 9$$

(450 As can be sold in a week, therefore 90 can be sold per day and as batches of 10 are being considered this becomes 9 batches of 10)

Similarly for the production of B:

$$2C_2 + 1C_4 \leqslant 11$$

(i.e. 11 batches of 10)

For the production of C:

$$3C_3 + 2C_4 \leqslant 9$$

(i.e. 9 batches of 10)

The total number of hours worked per day must not be more than 8, hence:

$$C_2 + C_3 + C_4 \leqslant 8$$

The inequalities are converted to equations by adding a variable to each. This variable must be either positive or zero. It is also true for all the variables, as the plant cannot be run for a negative number of hours.

The equations become

$$
\begin{aligned}
C_2 + 2C_3 + C_4 + R_1 &= 9 \\
2C_2 \qquad + C_4 \qquad + R_2 &= 11 \\
3C_3 + 2C_4 \qquad + R_3 &= 9 \\
C_2 + C_3 + C_4 \qquad + R_4 &= 8
\end{aligned}
$$

The "R" variables are known as the slack variables—they take up the slack in the inequality.

There are 4 equations in 7 unknowns with an infinity of solutions. The required solution is the one that produces maximum profit.

To find the profit using each combination:

1. **First process combination** (per hour)

Expenditure			
	1 A mould at £1	=	£1
	2 B moulds at £6	=	£12
	The machine rent at £2	=	£2
	Machine feed at £5	=	£5
	Total Cost		= £20

Income			
	10 As produced at 12s. each	=	£6
	20 Bs produced at 16s. each	=	£16
	Total income		= £22

therefore   Net Profit   = £2

2. Second process combination (per hour)

$$2\ A \qquad\qquad = £2$$
$$3\ C \qquad\qquad = £9$$
$$\text{Machine rent} = £2$$
$$\text{Machine feed} = £5$$

$$\text{Total Cost} = £18$$

$$20\ A\text{s produce} \quad £12$$
$$30\ C\text{s produce} \quad £12$$

$$\text{Total Income} = £24$$

therefore $$\text{Net Profit} \qquad = £6$$

3. Third process combination (per hour)

$$1\ A \qquad\qquad = £1$$
$$1\ B \qquad\qquad = £6$$
$$2\ C \qquad\qquad = £6$$
$$\text{Machine rent} = £2$$
$$\text{Machine feed} = £5$$

$$\text{Total Cost} = £20$$

$$10\ A\text{s produce} \quad £6$$
$$10\ B\text{s produce} \quad £8$$
$$20\ C\text{s produce} \quad £8$$

$$\text{Total Income} = £22$$

therefore $$\text{Net Profit} \qquad = £2$$

The Profit equation is:

$$P = 2C_2 + 6C_3 + 2C_4$$

(N.B. Number of hours of first combination $= C_2$, Profit per hour $= £2$, therefore Total Profit with this combination $= 2C_2$. Similarly for C_3 and C_4.)

No profit or loss accrues from the slack variables.

The problem is to maximise P

Rewrite the equations as follows:

$$R_1 = 9 - (\quad C_2 + 2C_3 + \quad C_4)$$
$$R_2 = 11 - (\ 2C_2 \qquad\quad + \quad C_4)$$
$$R_3 = 9 - (\qquad\qquad 3C_3 + 2C_4)$$
$$R_4 = 8 - (\quad C_2 + \quad C_3 + \quad C_4)$$
$$P = 0 - (-2C_2 - 6C_3 - 2C_4)$$

In tableau form (the independent terms, 9, 11, 9, 8 have been designated C_1, the Quantity column).

Labels	C_1	C_2	C_3	C_4	R_1	R_2	R_3	R_4
R_1	9	1	2	1	1			
R_2	11	2		1		1		
R_3	9		3 *	2			1	
R_4	8	1	1	1				1
P	0	−2	−6	−2				

* pivot (see below)

(i) Look for the most negative value in the control row, −6.
(ii) Divide each number in the C_1 column by the corresponding number in the column containing −6, i.e. C_3 column

$$\text{Ratio } C_1/C_3$$
$$R_1 \quad \tfrac{9}{2} = 4\tfrac{1}{2}$$
$$R_2 \quad \tfrac{11}{0} = \infty$$
$$R_3 \quad \tfrac{9}{3} = 3$$
$$R_4 \quad \tfrac{8}{1} = 8$$

The smallest positive ratio is 3, and hence the pivot is 3 in the C_3 column, R_3 row.
(iii) Divide the R_3 row by 3 and eliminate all the other elements in the pivot column. The pivot row becomes:

	C_1	C_2	C_3	C_4	R_1	R_2	R_3	R_4
C_3	3		1	$\tfrac{2}{3}$			$\tfrac{1}{3}$	

(iv) The tableau becomes

Labels	C_1	C_2	C_3	C_4	R_1	R_2	R_3	R_4	Ratio C_1/C_2
R_1	3	1 *	0	$-\tfrac{1}{3}$	1		$-\tfrac{2}{3}$		3
R_2	11	2		1		1			$5\tfrac{1}{2}$
C_3	3		1	$\tfrac{2}{3}$			$\tfrac{1}{3}$		∞
R_4	5	1	0	$\tfrac{1}{3}$			$-\tfrac{1}{3}$	1	5
P	18	−2	0	2					

* pivot (see below)

−2 is the most negative number in the control row; the ratio of C_1 to C_2 is found.

H

(v) Eliminate C_2 from all the rows except the R_1 row.
The tableau becomes

Labels	C_1	C_2	C_3	C_4	R_1	R_2	R_3	R_4	Ratio
C_2	3	1	0	$-\frac{1}{3}$	1		$-\frac{2}{3}$		
R_2	5	0		$1\frac{2}{3}$	-2	1	$1\frac{1}{3}$		
C_3	3		1	$\frac{2}{3}$			$\frac{1}{3}$		
R_4									
P	24	0	0	$1\frac{1}{3}$	$+2$		$+\frac{2}{3}$		

(vi) The control row is now all positive, so the procedure is complete and we have the optimal (best) solution. Any value other than zero for the variables C_4, R_1 and R_3 will give a lower value to P.

Hence the solution given by putting C_4, R_1 and R_3 equal to zero must be the maximum profit solution required.

Hence the solution is as follows:

1. Run combination 1 (C_2) for 3 hours.
2. Run combination 2 (C_3) for 3 hours.
3. Do not supply 50 of the requirement of B.
4. Do not work for 2 out of the available 8 hours in the day.
5. The fixed cost per day = £16

Hence Profit = £24 − £16 = £8

In the solution the third combination is not used, whereas there may have been a condition that it should be used for at least one hour per day, although this was not stated in the original problem.

In the P row the coefficient of C_4 is $1\frac{1}{3}$, which means a penalty of £$1\frac{1}{3}$. There is no point in using the combination for an hour and not changing the rest of the solution as it would produce 10 As and 20 Cs which cannot be sold. Although 10 Bs would be sold the net effect is to produce a loss of £12. The minimum penalty is to accept the £$1\frac{1}{3}$ penalty, and this is achieved by altering the solution by subtracting the C_4 column from the C_1 column and reinterpreting the solution.

In the P row also the coefficient of R_1 is 2, which means a penalty of £2 on R_1. R_1 is the slack on the make of A or the activity of not meeting the demand by one unit. However, if one could increase the demand for As this would be equivalent to letting R_1 have a negative value. In this case there is a meaning to this negative value, so it can be allowed. So R_1 can be made equal to -2 before R_4 becomes negative. This, then, is the limiting value.

In business organisations this is very useful information, as it suggests that an additional 20 As at 12s. (income = £12), if sold, would produce an additional £4 profit. This profit could be used to lower the price in order to make the price more competitive, and hence more attractive, to the potential customer. The R_1 column of figures is used to change the solution to achieve this result.

EXERCISE No. 24

1. A commando party consisting of five sergeants and 30 men has to pass a hill which is strongly defended by the enemy. There are three ways of approaching the hill: (*a*) to the North; (*b*) directly; and (*c*) to the South. Because of the terrain it is estimated that to the North groups of 6 or 12 men under a sergeant each could get past while probably losing 2 men each and using 100 and 150 rounds of ammunition respectively. On the direct approach the groups would be of 6, 12 or 24 men which would probably lose 1, 3 and 6 men respectively and use 200, 250 and 300 rounds of ammunition. To the South only groups of 6 men could make progress and would use 300 rounds of ammunition, but they would be unlikely to lose any men. Each group must have a sergeant in charge, but if any sergeant was not required for a group he would become supernumerary to one of the other groups. The party starts with 2,100 rounds of ammunition, but because of future requirements they do not wish to use more than one half, i.e. 1,050 rounds, in passing the hill.

How should they be split up to minimise the loss of men?

[**Hint.** Label the rows, Sergeants, Men, Ammunition, Loss of men and head the columns A, B, C, D, E, F, Sergeants, Men, Ammunition.]

Chapter 7

STATISTICS

1. Given certain facts and figures, the question then asked is "What conclusions can be drawn from them?"

Facts and figures may be presented in many ways. The best method in any given problem will be determined by the type of data. A false conclusion can often be drawn from correct facts. It is very important that the facts are presented in such a way that the sense is obvious and also true.

2. PIE CHARTS

These enable the reader to see in one glance the whole meaning of a set of numbers.

Example

A typical boarding school spent its money in a year in the following way:

    15% Administration, interest payments, etc.
    14% Upkeep of buildings, rates, overheads.
    31% Teachers' salaries and pensions.
    40% Food, heating, laundry, domestic staff.

The information as it stands is better visualised if presented as shown on the next page.

The circle has 360°

$$100\% = 360°$$

therefore $$1\% = \frac{360}{100} = 3·6°$$

$14\% = 14 \times 3·6 = 50·4°$ (Rates, etc.)
$15\% = 15 \times 3·6 = 54°$ (Administration, etc.)
$31\% = 31 \times 3·6 = 111·6°$ (Teachers' salaries, etc.)
$40\% = 40 \times 3·6 = 144°$ (Food, etc.)

Total 360   degrees

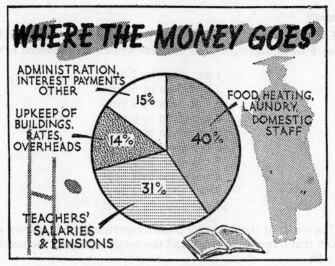

ADMINISTRATION,
INTEREST PAYMENTS
OTHER

UPKEEP OF
BUILDINGS,
RATES,
OVERHEADS

15%

14%

40%

31%

FOOD, HEATING,
LAUNDRY,
DOMESTIC
STAFF

TEACHERS'
SALARIES
& PENSIONS

WHERE THE MONEY GOES

Financial Times 5.1.61

The circle is shaded for better visual presentation.

The areas are proportional to the amount spent under each of the headings.

EXERCISE No. 25

Convert the data in the following questions into PIE CHARTS:

1. 30% of a group of people prefer to travel by train
   40% of a group of people prefer to travel by car
   20% of a group of people prefer to travel by coach

2. It is estimated that in this country we eat the following cereals for breakfast: Cornflakes 25%; Porridge 15%; Shredded wheat 12½%; Pre-sugared cereals 7½%; Other cereals 5%; None 35%.

3. A boy receives 10 shillings per week pocket money and allocates it as follows:

> 4s. towards a record player
> 2s. 6d. towards records
> 1s. 9d. towards holidays
> 1s. 3d. towards sweets
> 6d. towards other expenses

3. FREQUENCY

If when collecting data the same value occurs several times, then the frequency with which the various values occur is important.

Some events or values occur independently of each other, and these can be represented pictorially as in the following example:

Example

Each of a group of boys was asked to write down any 3 numbers from 1 to 10, inclusive. The numbers written are tabulated below:

1 was given by 2 boys
2 was given by 3 boys
3 was given by 2 boys
4 was given by 0 boys
5 was given by 9 boys
6 was given by 5 boys
7 was given by 6 boys
8 was given by 3 boys
9 was given by 1 boy
10 was given by 4 boys

The y-axis in the following picture represents the frequency with which that number occurred, and the x-axis represents the numbers 1 to 10.

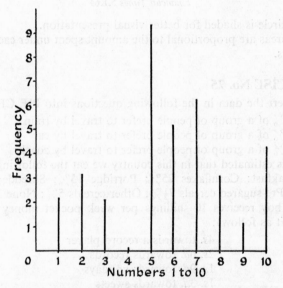

There is no obvious connection between any number and the number of times that it occurred, so there is nothing more to add to the picture.

MODE. The number that occurs most frequently in any set of data is called the mode. In the above example the mode = 5.

N.B. It is **not** the frequency with which it occurred. It occurred 9 times but the mode = 5.

4. FREQUENCY POLYGON

If the data represented on the x-axis is connected, then lines can be used to illustrate the frequency, and also the tops of the lines can be joined as in the following example:

Example

A newspaper boy counted the number of papers sold each day for 12 days with the following results:

6 papers sold on 4 days   10 papers sold on 25 days
7 papers sold on 6 days   11 papers sold on 15 days
8 papers sold on 18 days   12 papers sold on 1 day
9 papers sold on 20 days

This is represented on a graph as follows:

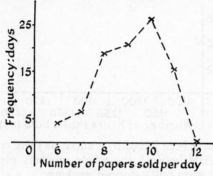

The mode in this case = 10 papers. It occurred most frequently; 25 times in fact.

The vertical lines in this example have been left out and only the top point in each case has been plotted. These points have been joined. A graph such as this is known as a FREQUENCY POLYGON.

5. FREQUENCY CURVE

A batch of electric-light bulbs was tested, and they were found to last for the following times:

90 bulbs lasted for 1,500 hours
100 bulbs lasted for 1,450 hours
120 bulbs lasted for 1,400 hours
140 bulbs lasted for 1,350 hours
160 bulbs lasted for 1,300 hours
200 bulbs lasted for 1,250 hours
180 bulbs lasted for 1,200 hours
150 bulbs lasted for 1,150 hours
140 bulbs lasted for 1,100 hours

This information is plotted on a graph as follows:

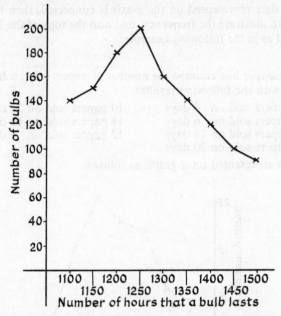

Number of hours that a bulb lasts

The points have been joined by a curve, as there could have been times intermediate between the whole numbers placed along the horizontal axis when bulbs stopped working.

A frequency polygon is used when no meaning can be attached to points between the values on the horizontal axis, as in the example in paragraph 4, viz. the newspaper boy can only sell whole newspapers.

A frequency curve is used when all points on the horizontal axis can have a meaning.

EXERCISE No. 26

1. In a school of 500 boys a record of the number of boys who reported sick at 9 a.m. over a period was as follows:

2 boys went sick on 2 days   9 boys went sick on 4 days
3 boys went sick on 6 days   10 boys went sick on 0 days
4 boys went sick on 10 days   11 boys went sick on 2 days
5 boys went sick on 14 days   12 boys went sick on 1 day
6 boys went sick on 15 days   13 boys went sick on 0 days
7 boys went sick on 13 days   14 boys went sick on 1 day
8 boys went sick on 8 days   20 boys went sick on 1 day

(No epidemic occurred.)
Construct a frequency polygon. Find the mode.

2. In an experiment the time of a certain event was measured by 24 boys. The following were the times recorded (in seconds):

6·2; 6·4; 7·1; 6·6; 6·8; 6·3; 7·0; 6·4; 6·3; 6·5; 6·8; 6·1; 6·9; 6·6; 6·4; 6·3; 6·2; 6·2; 6·6; 6·7; 6·4; 6·5; 6·3; 6·4

(i) Draw the frequency polygon.
(ii) What is the mode?

3. The takings in a shop for the first 6 months of a year were as follows:

Month	Jan.	Feb.	March	April	May	June
Total Sales	£440	£860	£1,240	£1,100	£1,680	£1,420

Construct a frequency polygon to illustrate the sales.

4. A certain component (an engine tail pipe) in an aeroplane was found to fracture as follows:

1 component fractured between   800 and   849 hours
7 components fractured between 1,000 and 1,049 hours
9 components fractured between 1,050 and 1,099 hours
14 components fractured between 1,100 and 1,149 hours
8 components fractured between 1,150 and 1,199 hours
4 components fractured between 1,200 and 1,249 hours
3 components fractured between 1,250 and 1,299 hours
2 components fractured between 1,300 and 1,349 hours
2 components fractured between 1,350 and 1,399 hours
1 component fractured between 1,400 and 1,449 hours

(i) Draw a frequency curve for the data.
(ii) What advice would you give the maintenance staff about replacing the component in aeroplanes in service

(a) in peacetime;   (b) on active service?

6. HISTOGRAM

The following times were recorded by 150 boys in running 100 yards:

1 boy ran 100 yards in 11·1 seconds
3 boys ran 100 yards in 11·2 seconds
6 boys ran 100 yards in 11·3 seconds
9 boys ran 100 yards in 11·4 seconds
10 boys ran 100 yards in 11·5 seconds
12 boys ran 100 yards in 11·6 seconds
15 boys ran 100 yards in 11·7 seconds
15 boys ran 100 yards in 11·8 seconds
16 boys ran 100 yards in 11·9 seconds

20 boys ran 100 yards in 12·0 seconds
24 boys ran 100 yards in 12·1 seconds
12 boys ran 100 yards in 12·2 seconds
10 boys ran 100 yards in 12·3 seconds
3 boys ran 100 yards in 12·4 seconds
4 boys ran 100 yards in 12·5 seconds

The boys are to be arranged in quarter-second groups. Those boys who run the 100 yards in 11·5 seconds are divided equally between the 2 groups 11·25–11·5 and 11·5–11·75. Similarly for those who run in 12 seconds and 12·5 seconds.

11–$11\frac{1}{4}$ seconds $1 + 3 = 4$ boys
$11\frac{1}{4}$–$11\frac{1}{2}$ seconds $6 + 9 + \frac{1}{2}(10) = 20$ boys
$11\frac{1}{2}$–$11\frac{3}{4}$ seconds $\frac{1}{2}(10) + 12 + 15 = 32$ boys
$11\frac{3}{4}$–12 seconds $15 + 16 + \frac{1}{2}(20) = 41$ boys
12–$12\frac{1}{4}$ seconds $\frac{1}{2}(20) + 24 + 12 = 46$ boys
$12\frac{1}{4}$–$12\frac{1}{2}$ seconds $10 + 3 + \frac{1}{2}(2) = 14$ boys
$12\frac{1}{2}$–$12\frac{3}{4}$ seconds $\frac{1}{2}(2) = 1$ boy

This is represented pictorially as follows:

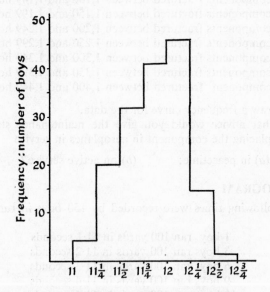

A graph such as this is called a HISTOGRAM.

The mode in this example corresponds to the range 12–$12\frac{1}{4}$ seconds. The interval 12–$12\frac{1}{4}$ seconds is sometimes called the MODAL CLASS.

N.B. A frequency curve may often be obtained from a histogram by joining the middle points of the tops of the columns. The decision as to which to use will depend on the type of data and personal preference.

EXERCISE No. 27

1. One Saturday in 1964 teams in the 4 divisions of the English Football League scored the following number of goals in a match:

0 goals scored by 21 teams
1 goal scored by 32 teams
2 goals scored by 21 teams
3 goals scored by 8 teams
4 goals scored by 2 teams
5 goals scored by 2 teams
6 goals scored by 1 team
7 goals scored by 1 team
over 7 goals scored by 0 teams

(i) Construct the frequency polygon.
(ii) What is the mode?

2. The following is a record of marks obtained by a group of boys in an examination:

43, 24, 62, 81, 70, 11, 56, 62, 37, 16, 22, 5, 95, 80, 71, 34, 74, 55, 20, 71, 44, 69, 43, 44, 17, 94, 1, 16, 59, 70, 81, 2, 60, 63, 26, 43, 41, 71, 64, 63, 84, 19, 28, 59, 51, 53, 54, 90, 91, 51, 54, 22, 80, 69, 57, 30, 31, 27, 18, 22, 71, 57, 36, 32, 29, 19, 61, 70, 49, 62, 63, 60, 39, 36, 38, 47, 82, 74, 76, 64, 66, 64, 48, 53, 39.

Tabulate, grouping in intervals of 10 marks 0–9, 10–19, 20–29, etc. Plot the result as a histogram and find the Modal class.

3. The following were the heights of 50 boys who entered a school in January 1960 (aged $13\frac{1}{2}$–14 years):

4 ft 8 in.; 5 ft $5\frac{1}{4}$ in.; 5 ft $4\frac{1}{2}$ in.; 5 ft 0 in.; 5 ft 2 in.; 5 ft 5 in.; 5 ft $3\frac{1}{4}$ in.; 5 ft 10 in.; 5 ft $2\frac{3}{4}$ in.; 5 ft 1 in.; 5 ft $6\frac{1}{4}$ in.; 5 ft $1\frac{3}{4}$ in.; 5 ft $1\frac{1}{2}$ in.; 5ft 2 in.; 4 ft $11\frac{1}{2}$ in.; 5 ft 6 in.; 5 ft $3\frac{3}{4}$ in.; 5 ft 1 in.; 4 ft 10 in.; 5 ft $3\frac{1}{2}$ in.; 5 ft $3\frac{1}{4}$ in.; 5 ft 3 in.; 5 ft $2\frac{1}{2}$ in.; 5 ft $4\frac{1}{4}$ in.; 5 ft $0\frac{1}{4}$ in.; 5 ft 8 in.; 4 ft 11 in.; 4 ft $11\frac{3}{4}$ in.; 5 ft $4\frac{1}{2}$ in.; 5 ft $7\frac{1}{2}$ in.; 5 ft $3\frac{3}{4}$ in.; 5 ft $1\frac{1}{2}$ in.; 4 ft $11\frac{1}{2}$ in.; 5 ft. 4 in.; 4 ft $11\frac{3}{4}$ in.; 4 ft $10\frac{1}{2}$ in.; 5 ft 1 in.; 5 ft 6 in.; 5 ft 4 in.; 5 ft 0 in.; 5 ft $3\frac{1}{2}$ in.; 5 ft $2\frac{1}{4}$ in.; 5 ft 1 in.; 5 ft $0\frac{3}{4}$ in.; 5 ft 5 in.; 4 ft $10\frac{1}{2}$ in.; 4 ft $10\frac{1}{2}$ in.; 5 ft $4\frac{1}{4}$ in.; 5 ft 4 in.; 5 ft $4\frac{3}{4}$ in.

Tabulate this information, grouping in intervals of one inch:

4 ft 7½ in.–4 ft 8¼ in., 4 ft 8½ in.–4 ft 9¼ in., 4 ft 9½ in.–4 ft 10¼ in., 4 ft 10½ in.–4 ft 11¼ in., 4 ft 11½ in.–5 ft 0¼ in., etc.

Plot the result as a histogram and find the modal class.

4. The heights of the same 50 boys in Question 3 were measured in December 1964 and found to be:

5 ft 7½ in.; 5 ft 11 in.; 6 ft 1 in.; 5 ft 10 in.; 5 ft 11 in.; 5 ft 9½ in.; 5 ft 11½ in.; 6 ft 2 in.; 5 ft 7 in.; 5 ft 11¼ in.; 6 ft 2½ in.; 5 ft 11¼ in.; 5 ft 8½ in.; 5 ft 8¾ in.; 5 ft 8¼ in.; 5 ft 10 in.; 5 ft 10½ in.; 5 ft 11½ in.; 5 ft 6½ in.; 5 ft 8 in.; 5 ft 10½ in.; 5 ft 10 in.; 5 ft 9 in.; 5 ft 9 in.; 5 ft 6 in.; 6 ft 3 in.; 5 ft 9 in.; 5 ft 7 in.; 5 ft 9 in.; 5 ft 11 in.; 5 ft 6½ in.; 5 ft 4¾ in.; 5 ft 8¼ in.; 6 ft 0½ in.; 5 ft 9 in.; 5 ft 10¼ in.; 5 ft 10½ in.; 6 ft 1¾ in.; 6 ft 2 in.; 5 ft 8½ in.; 5 ft 11¼ in.; 5 ft 10½ in.; 5 ft 10 in.; 5 ft 11 in.; 6 ft 1 in.; 5 ft 8 in.; 5 ft 7½ in.; 6 ft 1¼ in.; 5 ft 8 in.; 5 ft 11 in.

Tabulate this information, grouping in intervals of one inch, 5 ft 4½ in.–5 ft 5¼ in., 5 ft 5½ in.–5 ft 6¼ in., etc.

Plot the result as a histogram, on the same axes as Question 3. Find the modal class.

7. ARITHMETIC MEAN

In the example in paragraph six the most likely time that a boy would run 100 yards was seen to be between 12 and 12¼ seconds.

This is not the same as the average time, which is calculated as follows:

$$
\begin{aligned}
\text{Total times} = & (1 \times 11\cdot1) + (3 \times 11\cdot2) + (6 \times 11\cdot3) + (9 \times 11\cdot4) \\
& + (10 \times 11\cdot5) + (12 \times 11\cdot6) + (15 \times 11\cdot7) \\
& + (15 \times 11\cdot8) + (16 \times 11\cdot9) + (20 \times 12\cdot0) \\
& + (24 \times 12\cdot1) + (12 \times 12\cdot2) + (10 \times 12\cdot3) \\
& + (3 \times 12\cdot4) + (4 \times 12\cdot5) \\
= & \ 1,899\cdot2 \text{ seconds}
\end{aligned}
$$

Total number of boys = 160

Average time $= \dfrac{1,899\cdot2}{160} = 11\cdot245$ seconds

This is different from the mode, which was 12–12¼ seconds. The mode tells us the most frequently occurring group, and the AVERAGE or ARITHMETIC MEAN tells us something of the group as a whole and not of a special section of the group.

In general,

$$
\text{Arithmetic Mean} = \frac{\text{Sum of all values}}{\text{Number of values involved}}
$$

8. MEDIAN

The average value or Arithmetic Mean of the times of the boys in paragraphs six and seven does give us a time which was 11·245 seconds. In fact, no boy ran the 100 yards in this time.

Suppose we take the boy who is 80th in the table, starting from either end—this gives a boy in the 16 boys who took 11·9 seconds. This middle value, 11·9 seconds, is called the MEDIAN.

To summarise:

MODE: the value that occurs most frequently
MEAN: the average for all the values
MEDIAN: the middle or central value

(Approximately,

$$\text{Mode} = \text{Mean} - 3(\text{Mean} - \text{Median}))$$

EXERCISE No. 28

1. Find the median and mean for the following data:

(a) 2, 3, 3, 4, 5, 8, 9, 9, 11
(b) 2, 3, 5, 8, 12, 17, 23
(c) 4, 7, 8, 10, 11, 14
(d) 4, 10, 12, 18, 24, 26, 32, 36
(e) 8, -2, $1\frac{1}{2}$, $4\frac{1}{2}$, 3, -1, 0, $\frac{1}{2}$, $-1\frac{1}{2}$

2. The following donations were received by a charity:

£5,000	1 donation
£1,000	2 donations
£500	4 donations
£250	5 donations
£100	8 donations
£50	8 donations
£10	12 donations

Find: (a) the Mean; (b) the Median; (c) the Mode.

3. Using the data of Question 3 in Exercise No. 27, find:

(a) The Mean   (b) The Median

and using the approximate formula

$$\text{Mode} = \text{Mean} - 3(\text{Mean} - \text{Median})$$

find the mode and compare this value with the modal class obtained.

9. CUMULATIVE FREQUENCY

A frequency distribution can be converted to a CUMULATIVE FREQUENCY DISTRIBUTION by adding each frequency to the total of its predecessors.

Example

In an examination the marks obtained by a group of boys were as follows:

Examination marks (out of 100)	Number of Candidates
Not more than 10	5
Not more than 20	10 + 5 = 15
Not more than 30	18 + 15 = 33
Not more than 40	25 + 33 = 58
Not more than 50	39 + 58 = 97
Not more than 60	46 + 97 = 143
Not more than 70	36 + 143 = 179
Not more than 80	30 + 179 = 209
Not more than 90	15 + 209 = 224
Not more than 100	1 + 224 = 225

N.B. A mark of 10% is included in the first group.

The Cumulative Frequency curve or OGIVE is then plotted as follows:

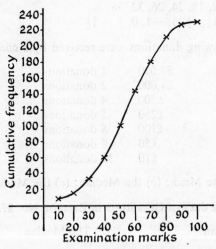

("Ogive" is a term used in architecture to describe a curve shaped like the one above.)

(i) The median of the group is the mark obtained by the 112·5th boy. The ogive shows that 112·5 boys got not more than 54 marks, it is therefore assumed that the 112·5th boy got 54 marks and therefore the median = 54

The difference between the 112·5th boy and the 113th boy is negligible for a large number of measurements.

(ii) The Pass mark is 45.

From the ogive the number of boys with not more than 44 is seen to be 72. Therefore 72 of the 225 boys fail, that is, $\frac{72}{225} \times 100\% = 32\%$, and therefore 68% pass.

The mark of 72 is called the 32nd percentile because 32% of the boys got 72 or less marks.

(iii) QUARTILES

(a) The 25th percentile is the mark obtained by not more than $\frac{25}{100} \times 225$ boys, i.e. 56($\frac{1}{4}$) boys.

From the ogive this mark is 39 marks.
The 25th percentile is called the LOWER QUARTILE.

(b) The 75th percentile is the mark obtained by not more than $\frac{75}{100} \times 225$ boys, i.e. 168$\frac{3}{4}$ boys = 169 boys

The ogive shows that 67 marks were obtained by these boys.
The 75th percentile is called the UPPER QUARTILE.

(c) Lower Quartile is 39 marks
Upper Quartile is 67 marks

(N.B. The quartiles are **not** the frequencies.)
The median is 54 marks.

EXERCISE No. 29

1. The following table gives the frequency distribution of the marks obtained in a test given to 600 candidates. Construct a table showing the cumulative frequency and draw a graph of the ogive. From your graph find the median and the quartiles.

By extending the division of the distribution into percentiles, obtain also the mark not reached by the lowest 40% of the candidates and the percentage passing if the pass mark is 55.

0–10	11–20	21–30	31–40	41–50	51–60
20	20	40	40	55	75

61–70	71–80	81–90	91–100	101–110	
80	120	90	40	20	

2. The following table gives the lengths of 800 corn cobs:

Not more than 5 in. long   —   10
Not more than 5·5 in. long   —   43
Not more than 6 in. long   —   113
Not more than 6·5 in. long   —   223
Not more than 7 in. long   —   399
Not more than 7·5 in. long   —   571
Not more than 8 in. long   —   695
Not more than 8·5 in. long   —   756
Not more than 9 in. long   —   788
Not more than 9·5 in. long   —   800

Find:
(i) the median
(ii) the lower quartile
(iii) the upper quartile
(iv) the difference between (iii) and (ii) (called the inter-quartile range)

3. The table shows the distribution of the marks of 648 candidates in a G.C.E. mathematics examination.

Mark	10	20	30	40	50	60	70	80	90	100
Number of candidates who scored less than this mark	8	34	104	190	310	450	543	615	638	648

Draw a graph (the "cumulative frequency" graph) to show these data, representing marks on the horizontal axis and the number of candidates on the vertical axis.

Use the graph to estimate:
(i) how many candidates scored less than 75 marks
(ii) the pass mark, if 60% of the 648 candidates passed
(iii) how many candidates failed to pass by only one mark?
[O. and C., "O" level July 1964]

10. DISPERSION

An average or mean value gives some information about a set of values or observations but often it is necessary to know how the observations are scattered around their average.

(a) RANGE. This simply gives the distance between the smallest and largest observations.

(b) INTER-QUARTILE RANGE. This is the distance between the lower and upper quartiles. In the example given in paragraph 9 the inter-quartile range is 39–67 marks.

(c) MEAN DEVIATION. The mean of a set of observations is calculated, and then the difference between each observation and the mean is found.

The method of working will be explained by using a very simple example.

Set of observations:

$$1, 2, 4, 5, 5\tfrac{1}{2}, 7, 7\tfrac{1}{2}, 8, 9\tfrac{1}{2}$$

The mean is $5\tfrac{1}{2}$.

The differences are calculated as follows, the $+$ or $-$ sign is ignored.

Deviations from Mean

$5\tfrac{1}{2} - 1 = 4\tfrac{1}{2}$

$5\tfrac{1}{2} - 2 = 3\tfrac{1}{2}$

$5\tfrac{1}{2} - 4 = 1\tfrac{1}{2}$

$5\tfrac{1}{2} - 5 = \tfrac{1}{2}$

$5\tfrac{1}{2} - 5\tfrac{1}{2} = 0$

$7 - 5\tfrac{1}{2} = 1\tfrac{1}{2}$

$7\tfrac{1}{2} - 5\tfrac{1}{2} = 2$

$8 - 5\tfrac{1}{2} = 2\tfrac{1}{2}$

$9\tfrac{1}{2} - 5\tfrac{1}{2} = 4$

Sum of Differences $= 20$

The number of observations $= 9$

MEAN DEVIATION $= \tfrac{20}{9} = 2\tfrac{2}{9}$

The MEAN DEVIATION is the average of the deviations from the mean.

(d) STANDARD DEVIATION

The best and most useful measure of scatter is the STANDARD DEVIATION.

In words it is:

The square root of the mean of the squares of the deviations of the observations from their arithmetic mean.

In symbols, $\quad \sigma =$ standard deviation

Let $\qquad \bar{x} =$ arithmetic mean

$\qquad\qquad x =$ any value

then $\qquad (x - \bar{x}) =$ deviation of an individual observation from the mean

$\qquad (x - \bar{x})^2 =$ square of the individual deviation

$\qquad \Sigma(x - \bar{x})^2 =$ sum of the squares of all the deviations

$\qquad\qquad N =$ number of observations

then $\qquad \sigma = \sqrt{\dfrac{\Sigma(x - \bar{x})^2}{N}}$

I

(e) VARIANCE

The square of the standard deviation is called the VARIANCE.

(f) The method of calculating the standard deviation depends on the type of observations and the number involved. For a very simple example the method is as follows:

To find the standard deviation of the first 9 natural numbers: 1, 2, 3, 4, 5, 6, 7, 8, 9

The arithmetic mean $= \bar{x} = 5$

x	$x - \bar{x}$	$(x - \bar{x})^2$
1	−4	16
2	−3	9
3	−2	4
4	−1	1
5	0	0
6	1	1
7	2	4
8	3	9
9	4	16

$$60 = \Sigma(x - \bar{x})^2$$

$$\sigma = \sqrt{\frac{60}{9}}$$

$$\sigma = 2{\cdot}582$$

N.B. The standard deviation is always measured from the mean and **never** from the median or mode.

EXERCISE No. 30

1. Find for the following sets of data:

(i) the range; (ii) the mean deviation; (iii) standard deviation.

(a) 1, 2, 3
(b) 1, 2, 3, 4, 5
(c) 1, 2, 3, 4, 5, 6, 7
(d) 2, 3, 5, 6, 7, 7, 8, 10, 10, 12

2. The mean daily sunshine for Falmouth and London for a period of 6 months in 1950 is given below:

	Jan.	Feb.	Mar.	Apr.	May	June
Falmouth (hours)	1·6	2·2	4·2	7·1	7·8	7·7
London (Kew) (hours)	0·8	2·4	4·5	5·6	5·8	8·6

Find for each the average number of hours' sunshine per day and the standard deviation.

11. (*a*) Another formula for standard deviation is

$$\sigma = \sqrt{\frac{\Sigma x^2}{N} - \bar{x}^2}$$

The proof is as follows:

Let the observations be x_1, x_2, x_3, x_4, x_5, etc., and the mean $= \bar{x}$.

Then the differences from the mean are $(x_1 - \bar{x})$, $(x_2 - \bar{x})$, $(x_3 - \bar{x})$, etc.

Squaring, we have

$$(x_1 - \bar{x})^2 = x_1^2 - 2x_1\bar{x} + \bar{x}^2$$

$$(x_2 - \bar{x})^2 = x_2^2 - 2x_2\bar{x} + \bar{x}^2$$

$$(x_3 - \bar{x})^2 = x_3^2 - 2x_3\bar{x} + \bar{x}^2$$

$$\cdot \qquad \cdot \qquad \cdot \qquad \cdot$$
$$\cdot \qquad \cdot \qquad \cdot \qquad \cdot$$
$$\cdot \qquad \cdot \qquad \cdot \qquad \cdot$$

Summing these we have

$$\Sigma(x - \bar{x})^2 = \Sigma x^2 - 2\bar{x}\Sigma x + N\bar{x}^2$$

Divide through by N as follows:

$$\frac{\Sigma(x - \bar{x})^2}{N} = \frac{\Sigma x^2}{N} - \frac{2\bar{x}\Sigma x}{N} + \bar{x}^2$$

but the mean value $= \dfrac{\Sigma x}{N} = \bar{x}$

$$\therefore \qquad \frac{\Sigma(x - \bar{x})^2}{N} = \frac{\Sigma x^2}{N} - 2\bar{x}^2 + \bar{x}^2$$

$$\therefore \qquad \frac{\Sigma(x - \bar{x})^2}{N} = \frac{\Sigma x^2}{N} - \bar{x}^2$$

$$\sigma = \sqrt{\frac{\Sigma x^2}{N} - \bar{x}^2}$$

(*b*) This is more useful when extended to a frequency distribution table, when the formula becomes

$$\sigma = \sqrt{\frac{\Sigma(fx^2)}{N} - \left[\frac{\Sigma fx}{N}\right]^2}$$

Example

Find the standard deviation of the observations in the following frequency distribution table:

Observation	Frequency
1	2
2	4
3	5
4	3
5	6

The following table is constructed:

x	f	fx	x^2	fx^2	
1	2	2	1	2	$N = \Sigma f = 20$
2	4	8	4	16	$\Sigma(fx) = 67$
3	5	15	9	45	$\Sigma(fx^2) = 261$
4	3	12	16	48	
5	6	30	25	150	
	20	67		261	

$$\sigma = \sqrt{\frac{261}{20} - \left(\frac{67}{20}\right)^2} = \sqrt{13\cdot05 - 11\cdot22}$$

$$= \sqrt{1\cdot83}$$

$$\sigma = 1\cdot353$$

12. THE USE OF AN ARBITRARY MEAN

In more complicated examples, especially those involving decimals such as 15·75, etc., much arithmetical labour can be avoided by working from an arbitrary mean and making a correction to the standard deviation found.

If σ = true standard deviation

Let s = fictitious standard deviation

         M = True Mean

         A = Arbitrary Mean

Then $\sigma^2 = s^2 - (M - A)^2$

Proof By definition

$$\sigma^2 = \frac{f_1(x_1 - M)^2 + f_2(x_2 - M)^2 + \ldots + f_n(x_n - M)^2}{f_1 + f_2 + \ldots + f_n}$$

and

$$s^2 = \frac{f_1(x_1 - A)^2 + f_2(x_2 - A)^2 + \ldots + f_n(x_n - A)^2}{f_1 + f_2 + \ldots + f_n}$$

therefore

$$(f_1 + f_2 + \ldots + f_n)(s^2 - \sigma^2)$$
$$= 2(M - A)(f_1 x_1 + f_2 x_2 + \ldots + f_n x_n)$$
$$+ (A^2 - M^2)(f_1 + f_2 + \ldots + f_n)$$

Thus

$$s^2 - \sigma^2 = 2(M - A)\left(\frac{f_1 x_1 + f_2 x_2 + \ldots + f_n x_n}{f_1 + f_2 + \ldots + f_n}\right) + A^2 - M^2$$

$$= 2(M - A)M + A^2 - M^2$$

$$= M^2 - 2AM + A^2$$

$$s^2 - \sigma^2 = (M - A)^2$$

Hence

$$\sigma^2 = s^2 - (M - A)^2$$

The use of this is shown in the following simple example:

Example

Find the standard deviation of the following measurements:

Measurement	Frequency
1·5	2
2·0	6
2·5	7
3·0	4
3·5	3

The following table is constructed. Let the Arbitrary Mean be 3:

x	f	fx	Deviation from 3	Deviation^2	Deviation^2 $\times f$
1·5	2	3·0	−1·5	2·25	4·5
2·0	6	12·0	−1·0	1·0	6·0
2·5	7	17·5	−0·5	0·25	1·75
3·0	4	12·0	0	0	0
3·5	3	10·5	+0·5	0·25	0·125
Totals	22	55·0			12·375

(a) True Mean $= \dfrac{fx}{f} = \dfrac{55\cdot0}{22} = 2\cdot5$

(b) Arbitary Mean $= 3$

(c) $(M - A) = -0\cdot5$

(d) $(M - A)^2 = (-0\cdot5)^2 = +0\cdot25$

(e) $s^2 = \dfrac{12\cdot375}{22} = 0\cdot5625$

(f) $\sigma^2 = s^2 - (M - A)^2$
$= 0\cdot5625 - 0\cdot25$
$\sigma^2 = 0\cdot3125$
$\therefore \sigma = 0\cdot559$

EXERCISE No. 31

1. Find the standard deviation of the following measurements of x:

x	8·5	9·0	9·5	10	10·5	11·0	11·5	12·0
Frequency	4	6	15	30	26	13	5	1

2. Find the mean and the standard deviation for the following observations:

Value in cms	0·8	0·85	0·9	0·95	1·0	1·05	1·10	1·15	1·20	1·25
Frequency	4	14	28	32	14	14	5	3	2	1

13. COEFFICIENT OF VARIATION

If we want to compare the scatter of different variables about their means it is useful to express the scatter in a form that is not dependent on the size of the variables. For example, cats and women may be relatively equally variable in length, but simply giving the standard deviations for sets or samples of each would not reveal this. The coefficient of variation is found by giving the standard deviation as a percentage ratio of the mean.

$$\text{Coefficient of Variation} = V = \frac{100\sigma}{M}$$

where M is the mean of the sample.

Example

Compare the relative variability of the following 2 sets of data:

(i) $\begin{cases} M_1 = 64 \\ \sigma_1 = 2\cdot4 \end{cases}$ (ii) $\begin{cases} M_2 = 25 \\ \sigma_2 = 2\cdot6 \end{cases}$

For (i) $V_1 = \dfrac{100 \times 2\cdot4}{64} = 3\cdot75$

For (ii) $V_2 = \dfrac{100 \times 2\cdot6}{25} = 10\cdot4$

Hence the data in (ii) are about 3·7 times as scattered relative to their mean as those in (i).

EXERCISE No. 32

1. Find the coefficient of variation for the following sets of data:

(a) 1, 2, 3
(b) 1, 2, 3, 4, 5
(c) 1, 2, 3, 4, 5, 6, 7.

(For σ see Question 1 of Exercise No. 30.)

2. Which of the two sets of data of Questions 1 and 2 of Exercise No. 31 is the more dispersed?

14. NORMAL DISTRIBUTIONS

(i) Suppose two coins are tossed simultaneously, then the probabilities are that in 4 throws we will have (T, T); (T, H); (H, T); (H, H).

That is

two tails   —once
one head, one tail—twice
two heads   —once

This is shown in the following histogram; the frequency polygon is obtained by joining the points at the centre of each range.

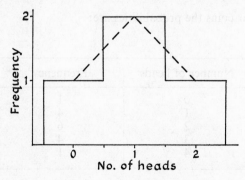

(ii) For three coins tossed simultaneously the probabilities are:

 Three tails or no heads —once

 Two tails and one head—three times

 One tail and two heads—three times

 Three heads —once

This is shown in the following histogram:

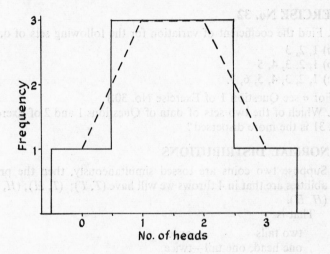

The frequency polygon is superimposed.

(iii) For four coins the probabilities are:

Number of heads	Frequency
0	1
1	4
2	6
3	4
4	1

and the histogram is as follows:

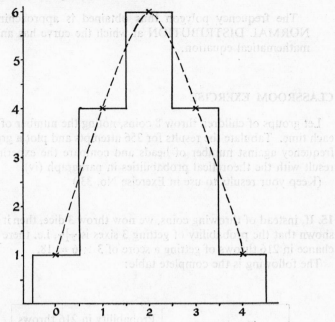

(iv) For 8 coins we have:

Number of heads	0	1	2	3	4	5	6	7	8
Frequency	1	8	28	56	70	56	28	8	1

The histogram and frequency polygon are as follows:

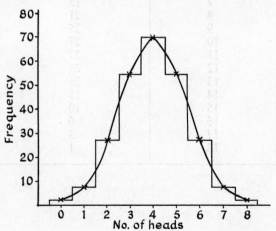

The frequency polygon thus obtained is approaching the NORMAL DISTRIBUTION at which the curve has an exact mathematical equation.

CLASSROOM EXERCISE

Let groups of children throw 8 coins, noting the number of heads each time. Tabulate the results for 256 attempts and plot a graph of frequency against number of heads and compare the experimental result with the theoretical probabilities in paragraph (iv).

(Keep your results to use in Exercise No. 33.)

15. If, instead of throwing coins, we now throw 3 dice, then it can be shown that the probability of getting 3 sixes is $\frac{1}{216}$, i.e. there is one chance in 216 throws of getting a score of $3 \times 6 = 18$.

The following is the complete table:

Total score	Probability in 216 throws of getting the score
3	1
4	3
5	6
6	10
7	15
8	21
9	25
10	27
11	27
12	25
13	21
14	15
15	10
16	6
17	3
18	1

The following is the frequency curve obtained:

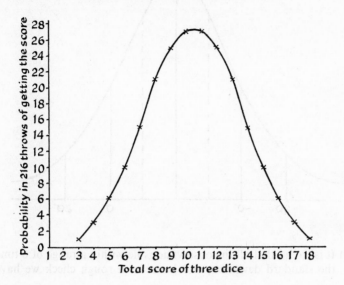

CLASSROOM EXERCISE

Let groups of children throw 3 dice, noting the total score each time. Plot the results obtained for 216 throws, 432 throws, and compare the graphs obtained with the graph shown for the theoretical values.

(Keep your results to use in Exercise No. 33.)

16. (i) The curve thus drawn is approximately normal distribution.

Many variables in biology are often distributed normally, for example, most intelligence tests give a distribution for intelligence quotients which is near that of a normal curve, down to an I.Q. of about 50.

The curve (see overleaf) is symmetrical and the median and the mode coincide with the mean.

(ii) In a true normal distribution we find: the area between $-\sigma$ and $+\sigma$ is 68% of the total area, i.e. 68% of all the observations lie within a distance equal to the standard deviation on each side of the mean.

(iii) The area between -2σ and $+2\sigma$ includes 95% of the observations.

(iv) The area between the dotted lines, -0.67449σ and $+0.67449\sigma$ has exactly half or 50% of the observations.

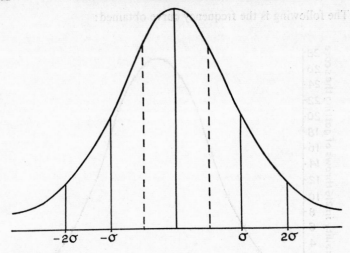

(v) It is found that all the observations lie within a range of 6 times the standard deviation, and hence as a rough check we have:

For a large number of observations the standard deviation should be approximately one-sixth of the range.

EXERCISE No. 33

1. With the results obtained in the questions in the preceding Classroom Exercises, find for *your* results:

(*a*) standard deviation
(*b*) the percentage of observations lying between $-\sigma$ and $+\sigma$
(*c*) the percentage of observations lying between -2σ and $+2\sigma$
(*d*) $\dfrac{\text{Range}}{6}$, [should be approximately σ]

Compare your results with the values given above.

2. The intelligence quotients of a group of children are given below:

I.Q.	48–57	58–67	68–77	78–87	88–97	98–107	108–117	118–127	128–137	138–147	148–157	158–167
Frequency	1	24	87	184	221	248	160	146	72	42	18	10

The average I.Q. $= 102.5$

(i) Construct a histogram
(ii) Divide the range by 6 to find the standard deviation
(iii) What percentage of the group lies between $-\sigma$ and $+\sigma$? [Find an approximate value]
(iv) What percentage of the group lies between -2σ and $+2\sigma$? [approximately]
(v) What can you say about the distribution?

17. RANKS

In many examinations, especially those of a competitive nature, the results are given in an "order of merit".
The candidates have been arranged in RANKS.
For example:

7 boys, A, B, C, D, E, F, G were ranked in Mathematics and Latin as follows:

Boy	A	B	C	D	E	F	G
Rank (Maths)	4	3	7	5	2	6	1
Rank (Latin)	1	6	5	7	3	2	4

It is often very useful to know whether a boy (or girl) who is good at Mathematics is also good at Physics or Music, say, on the average.
A measure of the agreement between two rankings is called the coefficient of correlation.

Let the coefficient of correlation $= r$

Let difference in rank $= d$

then   Sum of the square of the differences $= \Sigma d^2$

Let   Number of items being ranked $= N$

Then the formula is

$$r = 1 - \frac{6\Sigma d^2}{N(N^2 - 1)}$$

[The proof can be found in a more advanced textbook on statistics.]

The work is arranged as follows:

	Rank (Maths)	Rank (Latin)	d	d^2
A	4	1	3	9
B	3	6	3	9
C	7	5	2	4
D	5	7	2	4
E	2	3	1	1
F	6	2	4	16
G	1	4	3	9
				$52 = \Sigma d^2$

Hence
$$r = 1 - \frac{6 \times 52}{7(49 - 1)} = 1 - \frac{13}{14}$$

$$r = \tfrac{1}{14} = \cdot07144$$

$r = 1$ means complete correlation, i.e. absolute agreement;
$r = 0$ means no correlation, i.e. no agreement.

EXERCISE No. 34

1. In a beauty competition 3 judges ranked the finalists as follows:

	Miss A	Miss B	Miss C	Miss D	Miss E
Judge P	1	2	3	4	5
Judge Q	3	1	2	5	4
Judge R	4	3	1	2	5

Find the coefficient of correlation between:

(*a*) Judge P and Judge Q
(*b*) Judge P and Judge R
(*c*) Judge Q and Judge R

2. Compare the ranking in your class for any two subjects, for example, Mathematics and Physics; English and French.

ANSWERS

Chapter 1—Sets

Exercise No. 1

1. (a) {a, e, i, o, u}   (b) {1, 3, 5, 7, 9}
   (c) {March, May,}   (d) {2, 3, 5, 7, 11, 13, 17, 19}
   one is taken to be non-prime
2. (a) 26   (b) 5
3. (a) {9, 18, 27, 36, 45, 54, 63, 72, 81, 90}
   (b) {9, 18, 27, 36, 45, 54, 63, 72, 81, 90}   (c) Yes
4. (a) {Attlee, Churchill, Eden, Macmillan}
   (b) {I, V, X, L, C, D, M}   (c) {1, 4, 9, 16, 25, 36, 49, 64, 81}
5. (a) Equal   (b) Equal   (c) Equivalent
   (d) Unrelated   (e) Unrelated   (f) Equal
   (g) Equal   (h) Equal   (i) Unrelated
   (j) Unrelated
6. (a) True   (b) False   (c) False
7. (a) Yes   (b) Yes   (c) No   (d) No

Exercise No. 2

1. (a) {3, 5, 7}   (b) {3, 9}   (c) A   (d) φ
2. (a) {a b c}, {a b}, {a c}, {b c}, {a}, {b}, {c}, φ
   (b) {7, 11}, {7}, {11}, φ
   (c) {M J P}, {M J}, {MP}, {J P}, {M}, {J}, {P}, φ
   (d) {pqrs}, {p, q, r}, {p, q, s}, {p, r, s}, {q, r, s}, {pq}, {pr},
   {p, s}, {qr}, {q, s}, {r, s}, {p}, {q}, {r}, {s}, φ
3. (a) Many, e.g. set of boys in 1st XI
   (b) Many, e.g. set of numbers divisible by 9
   (c) Many, e.g. squares   (d) Many, e.g. set of atlases
4. (a)

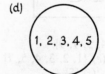

(b)

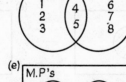

(c)

(d)

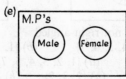

(e)

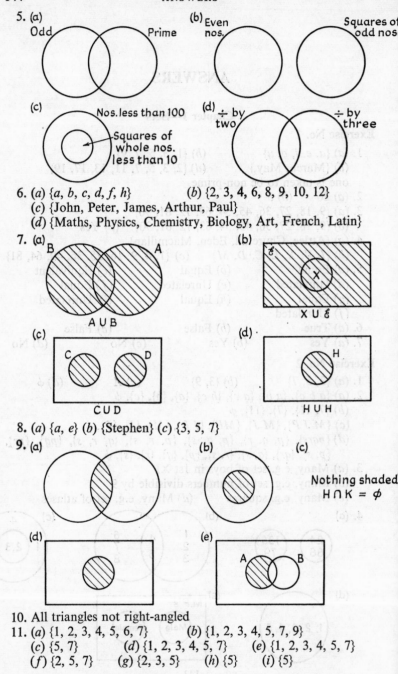

5. (a) Odd / Prime
(b) Even nos. / Squares of odd nos
(c) Nos. less than 100 / Squares of whole nos. less than 10
(d) ÷ by two / ÷ by three

6. (a) {a, b, c, d, f, h}   (b) {2, 3, 4, 6, 8, 9, 10, 12}
   (c) {John, Peter, James, Arthur, Paul}
   (d) {Maths, Physics, Chemistry, Biology, Art, French, Latin}

7. (a) A U B   (b) X U Ɛ
   (c) C U D   (d) H U H

8. (a) {a, e} (b) {Stephen} (c) {3, 5, 7}

9. (a)   (b)   (c) Nothing shaded H ∩ K = φ
   (d)   (e)

10. All triangles not right-angled
11. (a) {1, 2, 3, 4, 5, 6, 7}   (b) {1, 2, 3, 4, 5, 7, 9}
    (c) {5, 7}   (d) {1, 2, 3, 4, 5, 7}   (e) {1, 2, 3, 4, 5, 7}
    (f) {2, 5, 7}   (g) {2, 3, 5}   (h) {5}   (i) {5}

12.

(a)

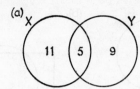

(b)

$n(X) = 16$

13. (a)

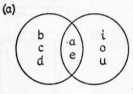

(b)

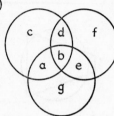

14. (a) 20%   (b) 50%   (c) 10%

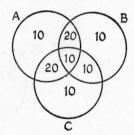

15. (a) {1, 2, 3, 9}   (b) 3   (c) 3

16. (a) 4   (b) 8   (c) 16   (d) 32   (e) 2^n

17. Arsenal *v.* Ipswich; Manchester Utd. *v.* Fulham;
    Spurs *v.* Stoke; Everton *v.* Bolton

18.   (a)   (b)

(c)   (d)

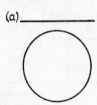 $\emptyset$, the null set

K

19. (a) 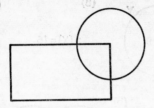   (b)

(c)   (d)

20. (a) {1, 2, 3, 4, 8}   (b) {2, 4}   (c) {2, 4, 5, 6, 7, 8, 9}
    (d) {1, 3}

21. 4

22. (a) $n(\mathscr{E}) = 120$
     $n(B) = 40, n(w) = 50$
     $n(C) = 60$

22. (b)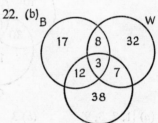

22. (c) 3

23. $x = 6$

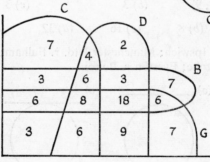

Exercise No. 3

2. Yes

4. (a) ϕ (b) {1, 2, 3, 4}   (c) {1, 2, 3, 4, 9}   (d) {5, 6, 7, 8}

5. $n(X \cup Y) = n(X) + n(Y) - n(X \cap Y)$

6. (i) meaningless   (ii) meaningless   (iii) always true
   (iv) never true   (v) always true   (vi) sometimes true

7. (i) A (ii) $\mathscr{E}$ (iii) ϕ (iv) A (v) ϕ (vi) A (vii) $\mathscr{E}$ (viii) B
8. (a) {3, 5}   (b) 30, 105, 15 True
   (c) $\pi(C) = 1,540$; $\pi(A \cap C) = 5$; Not true (H.C.F. = 10)
   (d) $\pi(P \cap Q)$ is H.C.F. of $\pi(P)$ and $\pi(Q)$ if no element of $P \cap Q'$ is a multiple or sub-multiple of $Q \cap P'$.

Chapter 2—Probability
Exercise No. 5

1. $\frac{1}{2}$ 2. $\frac{2}{7}$ 3. (a) $\frac{1}{13}$ (b) $\frac{1}{52}$ (c) $\frac{3}{13}$
4. (a) $\frac{2}{5}$ (b) $\frac{3}{5}$ (c) $\frac{23}{30}$ 5. (a) $\frac{3}{25}$ (b) $\frac{2}{5}$
6. (a) $\frac{11}{850}$ (b) $\frac{13}{850}$ 7. (a) $\frac{2}{5}$ (b) $\frac{11}{50}$
8. $\frac{24}{25}$ 9. $\frac{1}{216}$ 10. (a) $\frac{1}{5}$ (b) $\frac{7}{20}$ (c) $\frac{93}{100}$
10. (d) $\frac{11}{20}$ (e) $\frac{9}{10}$ 11. (a) $\frac{7}{25}$ (b) $\frac{4}{25}$ (c) $\frac{4}{175}$ (d) $\frac{7}{1050}$
12. (i) $\frac{16}{81}$ (ii) $\frac{1}{9}$ (iii) $\frac{4}{81}$ 13. $\frac{125}{216}$
14. (a) $\frac{13}{40}$ (b) $\frac{9}{800}$ (c) $\frac{27}{8000}$ (d) $\frac{273}{4000}$
15. (a) $\frac{29}{400}$ (b) $\frac{3}{200,000}$ (c) $\frac{181937}{200,000}$
16. (a) $\frac{16}{75}$ (b) $\frac{2}{25}$ (c) $106\frac{2}{3} \simeq 107; 40$
17. (a) $\frac{-5}{18}$ (b) $\frac{1}{6}$ 18. (a) $\frac{49}{50}$ (b) $\frac{189,189}{200,000}$
19. $\frac{21}{100}$ 20. (a) $\frac{1}{8}$ (b) $\frac{3}{8}$
21. (a) $\frac{4}{5}$ (b) $\frac{19}{40}$

Chapter 3—Number
Exercise No. 6

1. (a) 1; 111; $\cap$;
   11
   (b) v; v v v; <; v >; < v >
   v v
   (c) I; V; X; C; M (d) α; ε; i; ρ; α
2. I, Ꞁ, Ƨ, ⅃, Ɣ, ხ, 7, 8, 9
3. LXXVII

Exercise No. 7

1. No   2. (a) 32   (b) 23   (c) 19   (d) 27
3. (a) and (c)
4. (b) For $p - q$, $p > q$ is the condition (d) For $\frac{p}{q}$, $p = Cq$, [C is any natural number] is the condition

Exercise No. 8

1. (a) 3   (b) 11   (c) 5   (d) 7   2. See paragraph 1
3. The "shell" can be thought of as a sea shell or the sign of "Shell" petrol
4. (a) Addition is a binary operation for natural numbers
   (b) Commutative law for addition of natural numbers
   (c) Associative law for addition
   (d) Associative law for multiplication

(e) Commutative law for multiplication
(f) Commutative law for multiplication
(g) Distributive law for multiplication

7. As $p - q = 0$, one cannot divide by it

8. (a) $\frac{7}{17}$ (b) $\frac{2}{7}$ (c) $\frac{9}{5}$ (d) $\frac{5}{13}$

9. (a) $\frac{5}{12}$ etc.   (b) $\frac{55}{126}$ etc.   (c) $\frac{99}{70}$ etc.   (d) $\frac{137}{184}$ etc.

11. (a) $3 \cdot 666\ldots$ (b) $0 \cdot 4444\ldots.$
   (c) $1 \cdot 1666\ldots$ (d) $0 \cdot 28571428571428\ldots.$

12. (a) $\frac{1}{8}$ (b) $\frac{7}{9}$ (c) $\frac{3}{11}$ (d) $\frac{1}{7}$

13. (a) $5i$ (b) $4i\sqrt{2}$ (c) $-6i$ (d) $14i\sqrt{2}$
   (e) -3 (f) i (g) 2 (h) 4 (i) $-7i$

14. (a) ± 10 (b) $\pm 5\sqrt{3}$ (c) -6 (d) $\pm 2i$

15. (a) $10 + 6i$ (b) $6 + 10i$ (c) $7 - i$
   (d) $2 + 2i$ (e) $\frac{1}{2} - \frac{3}{2}i$ (f) -1

17. (a) $3 + i$ (b) 10 (c) $-3 - 5i$
   (d) $+1$ (e) $2i$ (f) 13

18. (a) $1 + i$ (b) $-i$ (c) $\dfrac{6 + 9i}{13}$

   (d) $\dfrac{-3 - 4i}{5}$ (e) $-i$ (f) $-\frac{1}{2}(i + 1)$

   (g) $\frac{1}{3}(\sqrt{2} + i)$ (h) $\frac{1}{7}(2 - i\sqrt{3})$ (i) $-\frac{1}{4}(i + \sqrt{3})$

19. (a) $\pm\sqrt{3}$ (b) ± 2 (c) $\pm i\sqrt{3}$

   (d) $\pm 2i$ (e) $+1$ (f) $\dfrac{-1 \pm i\sqrt{3}}{2}$

Exercise No. 9

1. (a) (base 3) $+$

	1	2
1	2	10
2	10	11

(base 3) $\times$

	1	2
1	1	2
2	2	11

(base 4) $+$

	1	2	3
1	2	3	10
2	3	10	11
3	10	11	12

(base 4) $\times$

	1	2	3
1	1	2	3
2	2	10	12
3	3	12	21

(c) (base 6) $+$

	1	2	3	4	5
1	2	3	4	5	10
2	3	4	5	10	11
3	4	5	10	11	12
4	5	10	11	12	13
5	10	11	12	13	14

(base 6) $\times$

	1	2	3	4	5
1	1	2	3	4	5
2	2	4	10	12	14
3	3	10	13	20	23
4	4	12	20	24	32
5	5	14	23	32	41

2. (a) (base 5) 1 2 3 4 10 11 12 13 14 20 21 22 23 24 30 31 32 33 34 40
   (b) (base 7) 1 2 3 4 5 6 10 11 12 13 14 15 16 20 21 22 23 24 25 26
   (c) (base 8) 1 2 3 4 5 6 7 10 11 12 13 14 15 16 17 20 21 22 23 24

3. (a) (base 3) 120, 121, 122, 200, 201, 202, 210, 211, 212, 220, 221
   (b) (base 4) 33, 100, 101, 102, 103, 110, 111, 112, 113, 120, 121
   (c) (base 9) 16, 17, 18, 20, 21, 22, 23, 24, 25, 26, 27
4. (i) 13   (ii) 113   (iii) 33   (iv) 49   (v) 241   (vi) 50
5. (i) 11010 (= 26 on scale 10)
   (ii) 10100010 (= 162 on scale 10)
   (iii) 101000000 (= 320 on scale 10)
6. (i) 111010   (ii) 1110100   (iii) 100000100
   (iv) 0·101   (v) 111·1   (vi) 10000·01
7. (i) 110010 (= 50 on scale 10)
   (ii) 10101100 (= 172 on scale 10)
   (iii) 10010 (= 18 on scale 10)
8. (i) 1001011 (= 75 on scale 10)
   (ii) 100011100011 (= 2275 on scale 10)
   (iii) 1110000101111 (= 7215 on scale 10)
9. (i) 111 (= 7 on scale 10)
   (ii) 1011 (= 11 on scale 10)
   (iii) 10110 (= 22 on scale 10)
10. (a) 1020   (b) 233   (c) 412
   (d) 45   (e) 340   (f) 46
   (g) 255   (h) 125   (i) 161
11. (a) 66   (b) 478_{10} (c) 422_{10} (d) 74_{10}
   (e) 134_{10} (f) 224_{10} (g) 130_{10} (h) 1752_{10}
12. More prime factors of base
13. $10p$ means $(1 \times P) + (0 \times 1) = P$ P_{10} means P
14. (a) 16_7 (b) 124_5 (c) 170_9 (d) $17X_{12}$
   (e) 414_5 (f) 17863_9 (g) 10248_{10} (h) 1245_7
15. (a) 21010_3 (b) 100300_4 (c) 10001_6
   (d) 102405_8 (e) 20861_{11} (f) 6037_{12}
16. (a) 11022_3 (b) 21202_4 (c) 4325_6
   (d) 73551_8 (e) $19X25_{11}$ (f) 5843_{12}
17. (a) 22000202_3 (b) 233123133_4 (c) 3434530_6
   (d) 326555102_8 (e) 19116885   (f) $Y68484_{12}$
18. (a) $11·00_3$ (b) $3·22_4$ (c) $11·23_6$
   (d) $22·43_8$ (e) $21·71_{11}$ (f) $2Y·7Y_{12}$
19. (a) Scale 9   (b) Scale 5   (c) Scale 11
   (d) Scale 12   (e) Scale 8   (f) Scale 7
20. (a) 10, 100, 110, 1000, . . . etc.   (b) 2, 11, 20, 22, . . . etc.
21. (a) 1, 11, 101, 111, . . . etc.   (b) 1, 10, 11, 21, . . . etc.
22. No   23. Yes, e.g. 54 on scale 7 = 39_{10}
24. (a) 26_7 (b) 143_7
25. (a) True   (b) True   (c) False   (d) True

Chapter 4—Simple Logic

Exercise No. 10

1. (a) Proper   (b) Common   (c) Common   (d) Proper
   (e) Common   (f) Common   (g) Common   (h) Common
   (i) Common

2. (a) False   (b) True   (c) True   (d) False
   (e) True   (f) True   (g) True   (h) True

3. (a) "It is cold"; "I am warm"
   (b) "The sea is inviting"; "I do not want to bathe"
   (c) "The car was an estate car"; "The car was a van"
   (d) "Richard likes guns"; "George likes guns"
   (e) "You do not like him"; "I do not like him"

4. (a) p: the sun is shining q: It is hot
$$p \to q$$
   (b) p: he gets cross q: his mouth will quiver
$$p \to q$$
   (c) p: He will marry her q: her father agrees
$$p \leftarrow q$$
   (d) p: It is true that he cries q: he is hurt
$$\sim p \leftrightarrow q$$
   (e) p: The culprit is Smith q: the culprit is Black
$$p \vee q$$
   (f) p: It is hot q: I want to swim
$$p \wedge q$$
   (g) p: It is cold q: it is very dry
$$p \wedge \sim q$$

5. (a) $T\ T\ T\ T$ (b) $F\ F$ (c) $T\ T$

6. (a) $p \to q$ (b) $q \to p$ (c) $q \leftrightarrow p$
   (d) $q \to \sim p$ (e) $\sim q \leftrightarrow \sim p$

7. (a) $T\ F\ T\ T$ (b) $T\ T\ F\ T$ (c) $T\ F\ F\ T$
   (d) $F\ T\ T\ T$ (e) $T\ F\ F\ T$

Exercise No. 11

1. (a) Not valid   (b) Not valid ["Some" does not include "all"]
     A valid conclusion might be "some Europeans do not drink wine"
   (c) Valid   (d) Not valid   (e) Not valid
   (f) Valid   (g) Not valid   (h) Not valid

Exercise No. 12

1. (i) If the sides of a triangle are all equal then the 3 angles of the triangle are equal
   (ii) If Barbara is Richard's mother, then Richard is Barbara's son
   (iii) If it is a rhombus, then the diagonals intersect at right angles

(iv) If 2 sides of a triangle are equal then the angles opposite to these sides will be equal

(v) It will rain if the wind is from the South-west (False)

(vi) If you are never lonely you buy "X" cigarettes (False)

2. (i) If the 3 angles of a triangle are not equal the sides are not equal

(ii) If Richard is not Barbara's son, then Barbara is not Richard's mother

(iii) If the diagonals of a parallelogram do not intersect at right angles, then it is not a rhombus

(iv) If the base angles of a triangle are not equal, then the sides opposite these angles are not equal

(v) If the wind is not from the South-west, then it will not rain rain (False)

(vi) If you do not buy "X" cigarettes, then you are lonely (False)

3. The truth depends on whether the premise is correct and we do not know that this is true

4. If you use X's soap then you will have soft hands and perhaps also be glamorous.

5. You will be admired (and have beautiful girls around you?) if you eat Y's chocolate

Chapter 5—Matrices

Exercise No. 13

1. (a) 87, 85, 34, 35 (b) 35, 55, 39, 20
   (c) 73, 39, 27, 18, 45, 36, 15, 12 (d) 43, 42, 21, 14
   (e) 21, 46, 10, 20, 17, 62, 6, 29
   (f) 27, 62, 13, 25, 3, 12, 1, 4
   (g) 45, 58, 18, 23, 57, 45, 26, 21, 54, 75, 18, 25
2. (a) Boon (b) Drive (c) May is out
   (d) Go now (e) This is easy
3. 62, 37, 28, 14, 25, 68, 10, 27, 99, 50, 37, 17, 80, 53, 33, 24, 33, 46, 16, 22, 13, 29, 6, 11

Exercise No. 14

1. $\begin{pmatrix} 2 & 5 \\ 3 & 4 \end{pmatrix}$

2. $\begin{pmatrix} 0 & 0 \\ 0 & 0 \end{pmatrix}$

3. $\begin{pmatrix} a+w & b+x \\ c+y & d+z \end{pmatrix}$

4. $\begin{pmatrix} 6 & -4 \\ 0 & 8 \end{pmatrix}$

5. $\begin{pmatrix} 3 & -6 \\ 9 & -12 \end{pmatrix}$

6. $\begin{pmatrix} pa & pb \\ pc & pd \end{pmatrix}$

7. $\begin{pmatrix} 2 & 7 \\ 6 & 0 \end{pmatrix}$

8. $\begin{pmatrix} -3 & 9 \\ 3 & 5 \end{pmatrix}$

9. $\begin{pmatrix} 2 & 2 \\ -2 & -2 \end{pmatrix}$

10. $\begin{pmatrix} 1 & -1 \\ 1 & -1 \end{pmatrix}$

11. $\begin{pmatrix} 4 & 6 \\ -6 & 4 \end{pmatrix}$

12. $\begin{pmatrix} 4 & 6 \\ -6 & 4 \end{pmatrix}$

13. They are the same. Multiplication by $\begin{pmatrix} 2 & 0 \\ 0 & 2 \end{pmatrix}$ is the same as the

scalar multiplication of the matrix $\begin{pmatrix} 2 & 3 \\ -3 & 2 \end{pmatrix}$ by the scalar 2

14. $\begin{pmatrix} a & b \\ c & d \end{pmatrix}$

15. (a) $\begin{pmatrix} 3 & 3 \\ 8 & 8 \end{pmatrix}$ (b) $\begin{pmatrix} 3 & 3 \\ 8 & 8 \end{pmatrix}$ (c) $\begin{pmatrix} 6 & 9 \\ 16 & 23 \end{pmatrix}$ (d) $\begin{pmatrix} 10 & 7 \\ 28 & 19 \end{pmatrix}$

16. (a) $\begin{pmatrix} 1, & 1 \\ 10, & 8 \end{pmatrix}$ (b) $\begin{pmatrix} 10, & 8 \\ 32, & 26 \end{pmatrix}$ (c) $\begin{pmatrix} 4, & 3 \\ 10, & 13 \end{pmatrix}$

(d) $\begin{pmatrix} 6, & 5 \\ 22, & 13 \end{pmatrix}$ (e) $\begin{pmatrix} 10, & 8 \\ 32, & 26 \end{pmatrix}$ (f) Yes

(g) $\begin{pmatrix} 2, & 4 \\ 16, & 34 \end{pmatrix}$ (h) $\begin{pmatrix} 4, & 5 \\ 6, & 13 \end{pmatrix}$ (i) $\begin{pmatrix} -2, & -1 \\ 10, & 21 \end{pmatrix}$

(j) $\begin{pmatrix} 2, & 4 \\ 16, & 34 \end{pmatrix}$ (k) Yes   (l) No

Exercise No. 15

1. (a) 14   (b) 5   (c) −1   (d) −15

(e) $pq - ab$ (f) −13   (g) 1   (h) 0   (i) 9

2. (a) $(\frac{4}{14} \quad -\frac{2}{14})$ (b) $\begin{pmatrix} -\frac{1}{5} & \frac{3}{5} \\ -\frac{1}{5} & -\frac{2}{5} \end{pmatrix}$ (c) $\begin{pmatrix} -6 & 1 \\ 1 & 0 \end{pmatrix}$

(d) $\begin{pmatrix} \frac{1}{5} & 0 \\ \frac{2}{15} & -\frac{1}{3} \end{pmatrix}$ (e) $\begin{pmatrix} \dfrac{b}{pq - ab} & \dfrac{-q}{pq - ab} \\ \dfrac{p}{pq - ab} & \dfrac{-a}{pq - ab} \end{pmatrix}$

(f) $\begin{pmatrix} -\frac{7}{13} & \frac{3}{13} \\ \frac{2}{13} & \frac{1}{13} \end{pmatrix}$ (g) $\begin{pmatrix} 0 & -1 \\ 1 & 0 \end{pmatrix}$

(h) It has no inverse, as the determinant = 0

(i) $\begin{pmatrix} \frac{1}{3} & 0 \\ 0 & \frac{1}{3} \end{pmatrix}$

4. (a) False   (b) False   (c) True   (d) False

Exercise No. 16

1. (a) $\begin{pmatrix} 8 \\ 1 \end{pmatrix}$ (b) $\begin{pmatrix} 7 \\ 3 \end{pmatrix}$ (c) (1, 5)   (d) $\begin{pmatrix} 11 \\ -4 \end{pmatrix}$

(e) Impossible as there are 2 columns in the first matrix but only 1 row in the second

(f) (2, 3)

2. (a) $\begin{pmatrix} 15 & 6 \\ -3 & -3 \end{pmatrix}$ (b) $\begin{pmatrix} 6a \\ 3a \end{pmatrix}$ (c) $\begin{pmatrix} 0 \\ 25 \\ -6 \end{pmatrix}$

(d) Impossible as there is 1 column in the first matrix and 3 rows in the second

(e) $\begin{pmatrix} -3 & -1 & +1 \\ -1 & +2 & -2 \\ +5 & +1 & -2 \end{pmatrix}$

Exercise No. 17

1. (a) $x = 2, y = 3$, or $\begin{pmatrix} 2 \\ 3 \end{pmatrix}$ (b) $x = 2, y = 5$, or $\begin{pmatrix} 2 \\ 5 \end{pmatrix}$

(c) No unique solution as the determinant is zero

(d) $x = -2, y = +2$, or $\begin{pmatrix} -2 \\ +2 \end{pmatrix}$

(e) $x = -3, y = 1\frac{1}{2}$, or $\begin{pmatrix} -3 \\ 1\frac{1}{2} \end{pmatrix}$

(f) $x = 3, y = -6$, or $\begin{pmatrix} 3 \\ -6 \end{pmatrix}$

(g) $x = -\frac{1}{2}, y = +\frac{1}{2}$, or $\begin{pmatrix} -\frac{1}{2} \\ +\frac{1}{2} \end{pmatrix}$

Exercise No. 18

1. (a) True   (b) False

Exercise No. 19

1. (a)

	apples	bananas	cu-cumbers	to-matoes	lettuce
Mrs A	2	3	1	0	0
Mrs B	1	0	2	2	1
Mrs C	0	2	$\frac{1}{2}$	1	2

(b) The price column vector is

	shillings
apples	$\frac{1}{2}$
bananas	$1\frac{1}{2}$
cucumbers	2
tomatoes	$2\frac{1}{2}$
lettuce	1

Mrs A's bill is 7s. 6d.
Mrs B's bill is 10s. 6d.
Mrs C's bill is 8s. 6d.

2. (ii)

coal (cwt.)	17
anthracite (cwt.)	36
logs (load)	4
coke (cwt.)	36

(iii) 4 tons 9 cwt.

(iv)

coal	$£\frac{6}{10}$	Smith	£22
anthracite	$\frac{7}{8}$	Jones	£19 4s.
logs	2	Brown	£20
coke	$\frac{3}{4}$	West	£14 10s.

(v) £75 14s.

3. (i)

	No. 1	No. 2	No. 3	No. 4
Pudding	1	2	2	0
Sherry	1	1	2	0
Crackers	1	1	2	0
Brandy	0	1	1	2
Cigars	0	0	1	2

(ii) Pudding $\begin{pmatrix} 29 \\ 27 \\ 27 \\ 14 \\ 12 \end{pmatrix}$
    Sherry
    Crackers
    Brandy
    Cigars

(iii) £77 18s. 6d.

Class discussion question

(a) Reflection in the x-axis

(b) $\begin{pmatrix} X \\ Y \end{pmatrix} = B \begin{pmatrix} x \\ y \end{pmatrix}$

$B = \begin{pmatrix} \cos 90 & -\sin 90 \\ \sin 90 & \cos 90 \end{pmatrix} = \begin{pmatrix} 0 & -1 \\ 1 & 0 \end{pmatrix}$

(c) $A \cdot B = \begin{pmatrix} 0 & -1 \\ -1 & 0 \end{pmatrix}$

$B \cdot A = \begin{pmatrix} 0 & 1 \\ 1 & 0 \end{pmatrix}$

(d) $P = \begin{pmatrix} -3 \\ -5 \end{pmatrix}$; $Q = \begin{pmatrix} 3 \\ 5 \end{pmatrix}$

The equation of the line in which P is the reflection of Q is
$$y = -\tfrac{3}{5}x$$

Exercise No. 20

1. (i) $\begin{pmatrix} 5 \\ 3 \end{pmatrix}$ (ii) $\begin{pmatrix} -6 \\ 4 \end{pmatrix}$ (iii) $\begin{pmatrix} -6 \\ 9 \end{pmatrix}$ (iv) $\begin{pmatrix} -4 \\ -12 \end{pmatrix}$

2. (a) $\begin{pmatrix} 2 \\ 1 \end{pmatrix}$ (b) $\begin{pmatrix} 4 \\ 2 \end{pmatrix}$ (c) $\begin{pmatrix} -1 \\ 2 \end{pmatrix}$ (d) $\begin{pmatrix} 10 \\ -5 \end{pmatrix}$

3. (a) Yes   (b) Yes   (c) Yes   (d) No

4. $\begin{pmatrix} 10 \\ -5 \end{pmatrix}$; $\begin{pmatrix} 16 \\ -8 \end{pmatrix}$; $\begin{pmatrix} 14 \\ -7 \end{pmatrix}$; $\begin{pmatrix} -10 \\ 5 \end{pmatrix}$; $\begin{pmatrix} 0 \\ 0 \end{pmatrix}$; $\begin{pmatrix} 4 \\ -2 \end{pmatrix}$

5. No

6. (a) (7, 3)   (b) (2, 5)   (c) $\begin{pmatrix} 0 \\ 3 \end{pmatrix}$ (d) $\begin{pmatrix} 3 \\ 6 \end{pmatrix}$

Exercise No. 21

1. (a) $\begin{pmatrix} 1 \\ -1 \\ 2 \end{pmatrix}$ (b) $\begin{pmatrix} -2 \\ 1 \\ 3 \end{pmatrix}$ (c) $\begin{pmatrix} 2 \\ -1 \\ 3 \end{pmatrix}$

2. $2P + Q = R$

3. No; the matrix is "singular"

Chapter 6—Linear Programming

Exercise No. 22

1. (a) (i) $10\tfrac{2}{3}$ (ii) 4   (iii) $10\tfrac{2}{3}$
     (iv) $10\tfrac{2}{3}$ (v) $13\tfrac{1}{3}$ (vi) $21\tfrac{1}{3}$
(b) 0

2. (i) 4   (ii) 5   (iii) 7
    (iv) 9   (v) 9   (vi) 6
3. (i) 12   (ii) 22   (iii) 16   (iv) 32   (v) 22
4. (i) 6   (ii) 9   (iii) 8
5. (i) (Min: 14) (Max: 26)   (ii) (Min: 26) (Max: 74)
    (iii) (Min: 26) (Max: 52)   (iv) (Min: 56) (Max: 172)
    (v) (Min: 38) (Max: 116)
6. £1,900
7. (i) $\frac{3}{4}x + \frac{1}{4}y \leqslant 60$ (in lb.)   (ii) $\frac{1}{4}x + \frac{3}{4}y \leqslant 30$ (in lb.)
    (iii) Profit $(P) = 3x + 6y$ (in pence)
    (iv) Maximum Profit = £1 6s. 3d.
8. (i) Cost = $6x + 3y$ (in pence)   (ii) $6x + 3y < 60$
    (iii) $x \geqslant 4; y > 2x$ (iv) (4, 9); (4, 10); (4, 11)
9. 2 "standard" size pills and 8 "kill" size pills
10. 41

Exercise No. 23

1. (a) 39   (b) 5   (c) 34
    (d) 390 (when $x_1 = 0$, $x_2 = 75$, $x_3 = 15$)
2. $x_1 = 2$, $x_2 = 0$, $x_3 = 0$, $x_4 = 0$, $x_5 = 3$
    Introduction of x_2 or x_4 would make x_3 negative

Exercise No. 24

1. 1 party of 12 to North   3 parties of 6 to South
    1 sergeant supernumerary   Loss = 2 men

Chapter 6—Statistics
Exercise No. 25

1. Train, 108°; Car, 144°; Coach, 72°; No preference, 36°
2. Cornflakes, 90°; Porridge, 54°; Shredded wheat, 45°; Pre-
    sugared cereals, 27°; Other cereals, 18°; None, 126°
3. Record player, 144°; Records, 90°; Holidays, 63°; Sweets, 45°;
    Other expenses, 18°

Exercise No. 26

1. Mode = 6 (boys)
2. (ii) Mode = 6·4 seconds
3. (ii) (a) Replace after 600 hours (75% of safe working life)
        (b) Replace after perhaps 700 hours (approx. $87\frac{1}{2}$% of safe
            working life)

Exercise No. 27

1. Mode = 1 goal
2. Modal Class = 60–69 marks
3. Modal Class = 5 ft $3\frac{1}{2}$ in.–5ft $4\frac{1}{4}$ in.
4. Modal Class = 5 ft $10\frac{1}{2}$ in.–5 ft $11\frac{1}{4}$ in.

Exercise No. 28

1. (a) median $= 5$; mean $= 6$
   (b) median $= 8$; mean $= 10$
   (c) median $= 9$; mean $= 9$
   (d) median $= 21$; mean $= 20\frac{1}{4}$
   (e) median $= \frac{1}{2}$; mean $= 1\frac{4}{9}$
2. (a) Mean $= £289\ 5s.$ (b) Median $= £75$ (c) Mode $= £10$
3. (a) Mean $= 5$ft $2\cdot53$ in.   (b) Median $= 5$ft $2\cdot75$ in.
   (c) Mode $= 5$ft $3\cdot19$ in. (Modal Class $= 5$ ft $3\frac{1}{2}$ in.–5ft $4\frac{1}{4}$ in.)

Exercise No. 29

1. Median $= 67$ marks   Lower quartile $= 46$ marks
   Upper quartile $= 80$ marks
   Mark not reached by lowest $40\% = 58$
   65% of candidates pass
2. (i) 7 in.   (ii) $6\cdot43$ in.   (iii) $7\cdot63$ in.   (iv) $1\cdot2$ in.
3. (i) 585 candidates   (ii) 55 marks   (iii) 19 candidates

Exercise No. 30

1. (a) Range $= 1$ to 3; Mean Deviation $= \frac{2}{3} = 0\cdot6667$; Standard
       Deviation $= \sqrt{\frac{2}{3}} = 0\cdot817$
   (b) Range $= 1$ to 5; Mean Deviation $= 1\cdot2$; Standard Devia-
       tion $= \sqrt{2} = 1\cdot414$
   (c) Range $= 1$ to 7; Mean Deviation $= 1\frac{5}{7} = 1\cdot7143$; Standard
       Deviation $= 2$
   (d) Range $= 2$ to 12; Mean Deviation $= 2\cdot4$; Standard Devia-
       tion $= 3$
2. Average hours sunshine per day for Falmouth $= 5\cdot1$; Standard
   Deviation $= 2\cdot566$
   Average hours sunshine per day for London $= 4\cdot62$; Standard
   Deviation $= 2\cdot5$

Exercise No. 31

1. $0\cdot7134$ 2. Mean $= 0\cdot9573$; $\sigma = 0\cdot08854$

Exercise No. 32

1. (a) $V = 40\cdot85$ (b) $V = 47\cdot13$ (c) $V = 50$
2. $V_1 = 0\cdot7021$, $V_2 = 9\cdot262$
   Hence the second set of data are about 13 times as scattered
   relative to their mean as are those in the first set.

Exercise No. 33

2. (ii) $\sigma = 20$ (iii) 65–66% approx.   (iv) 95% approx
   (v) Normal distribution with the mean on the high side: by
       definition it should be $= 100$

Exercise No. 34

1. (a) $0\cdot6$ (b) $0\cdot1$ (c) $0\cdot2$

INDEX